Glencoe

CHEMISTRY
MATTER AND CHANGE

Small-Scale Laboratory Manual

Teacher Edition

Glencoe McGraw-Hill

New York, New York   Columbus, Ohio   Woodland Hills, California   Peoria, Illinois

A GLENCOE PROGRAM

Glencoe
CHEMISTRY
MATTER AND CHANGE

Hands-On Learning:
Laboratory Manual, SE/TE
Forensics Laboratory Manual, SE/TE
CBL Laboratory Manual, SE/TE
Small-Scale Laboratory Manual, SE/TE
ChemLab and MiniLab Worksheets

Review/Reinforcement:
Study Guide for Content Mastery, SE/TE
Solving Problems: A Chemistry Handbook
Reviewing Chemistry
Guided Reading Audio Program

Applications and Enrichment:
Challenge Problems
Supplemental Problems

Assessment:
Chapter Assessment
MindJogger Videoquizzes (VHS)
TestCheck Software, Windows/Macintosh

Teacher Resources:
Lesson Plans
Block Scheduling Lesson Plans
Spanish Resources
Section Focus Transparencies and Masters
Math Skills Transparencies and Masters
Teaching Transparencies and Masters
Solutions Manual

Technology:
Chemistry Interactive CD-ROM
Vocabulary PuzzleMaker Software,
    Windows/Macintosh
Glencoe Science Web site:
science.glencoe.com

Send all inquiries to:
Glencoe/McGraw-Hill
8787 Orion Place
Columbus, OH 43240-4027

ISBN 0-07-824529-X
Printed in the United States of America.
 4 5 6 7 8 9 10   045   09 08 07 06 05 04

Contents

Laboratory Activities

To the Teacher

This *Small-Scale Laboratory Manual* contains 20 student activities and is designed for use with selected chapters in the ***Chemistry: Matter and Change Student Edition.*** This lab manual provides an alternative means of carrying out activities directly correlated with chapters in the textbook. Chapter references are listed at the beginning of each activity. Sample data and answers to questions can be found on the Teacher Guide pages at the end of this manual.

Using chemicals for teaching chemistry or biochemistry at the high school level is presently facing several problems at once. Concern for student safety, environmental questions, cost of materials, and the necessity of adhering to a prescribed curriculum have all worked to make the laboratory program difficult to carry out. Still, the "lab" is the most tangible, best remembered, and most visible aspect of science instruction.

When you have a limited time and a limited budget, microscale/small-scale chemistry provides a safe, inexpensive, and time-efficient means to conduct a biochemical laboratory activity.

Laboratory activities and experiments that use micro-amounts of chemicals provide a way to involve students in observation and manipulation of some substances that might otherwise be regarded as hazardous. Because drastically reduced amounts of chemicals are used, safety is greatly increased. Likewise, the expense of running a laboratory program is reduced. As with traditional laboratories using chemicals, all processes should be conducted with safety goggles and protective clothing.

Advantages of incorporating microscale/small-scale chemistry into the learning environment include the

- reduction in the cost of chemicals.
- reduction of possible fire and explosion danger.
- reduction of chemical waste disposal costs.
- introduction of experiments where chemicals once thought to be too expensive or hazardous can be made available with the reduced amounts.
- recycling products for future experiments (plan ahead and use it again).
- introduction of less expensive glassware.
- reduction of exposure to toxic materials.

Using the Laboratory Manual

Using the Laboratory Manual

Microscale/small-scale chemistry uses smaller amounts of chemicals than do other chemistry methods. The hazards of glass have been minimized by the use of plastic labware. If a chemical reaction must be heated, hot water will provide the needed heat. Open flames or burners are seldom used in small-scale chemistry techniques. By using microscale/small-scale chemistry, you will be able to do more activities and have a safe environment in which to work.

Microscale/small-scale chemistry uses two basic tools, the microplate and the plastic pipette. A microplate is a sturdy plastic tray that has shallow wells arranged in rows (running across) and columns (running up and down). These wells are used instead of test tubes, flasks, and beakers. Some microplates have 96 wells, and other microplates have 24 larger wells.

Microscale/small-scale chemistry uses a pipette made of a form of plastic that is soft and very flexible. The most useful property of the pipette is the fact that the stem can be stretched without heating into a thin tube. If the stem is stretched and then cut with scissors, the small tip will deliver a tiny drop of reagent. You may also use a pipette called a microtip pipette, which has been pre-stretched at the factory. It is not necessary to stretch a microtip pipette.

The pipette can be used over and over again simply by rinsing the stem and bulb between reagents. The plastic inside the pipette is non-wetting and does not hold water or solutions the way glass does.

Safety and Disposal in Small-Scale Chemistry

Using microscale/small-scale chemistry techniques means that dispensing liquids from plastic dropper bottles greatly reduces many spills. Accidental glass container breakage and fire hazards are eliminated, and air quality is improved due to smaller amounts of vapor escaping. Although some liquid is lost due to vaporization during both techniques, the microscale/small-scale chemistry technique reduces hazardous organic chemicals that must be recovered and disposed of properly. In addition, this technique represents a responsible step in reducing environmental pollutants. In the science storeroom, chemicals in smaller containers (approximately 10 percent of the size used in large-scale chemistry) reduce the need for storage space.

Collect all chemical solutions, precipitates, and rinse solutions in a polyethylene dishpan or similar container devoted to that purpose. Retain the solutions until the end of the period or day. In the fume hood, set up a hot plate with a 1-L or 2-L beaker. Pour the collection of solutions into the beaker. Turn the hot plate on low and allow the beaker to heat with the hood running and the hood door closed. The liquids and volatiles in the mixture will evaporate, leaving dried chemicals. Allow the beaker to cool. Continue to add solutions and waste until the beaker is 2/3 full. Treat the waste as heavy metal waste. *Dispose of the beaker and its dry contents in an approved manner. Review the Disposal Guidelines on pages 6T–10T.*

Chemical Safety and Disposal

The teaching of chemistry requires the use of certain supplies and safety equipment if a safe classroom is to be maintained.

Safety Equipment

As a chemistry teacher, you should be familiar with the use and maintenance of the following equipment.

Fume Hoods

Each laboratory facility and preparation room where chemicals are used should be equipped with a fume hood. No open face fume hood with a low face velocity can provide complete safety against events that take place in the hood. However, a properly designed hood in a properly ventilated room can provide adequate protection. To provide proper protections, follow these recommended guidelines.

- Keep the interior light on so that the working area is properly illuminated.
- Check the exhaust system—air movement is inward and upward in the hood.
- Conduct all portions of the experiment that cause contaminants to form inside the hood.
- Large objects should not be placed directly on the hood's working surface. Use blocks under the large object to allow proper airflow under the object.
- Move the vertical sash to the lowest position that allows access so that manipulation is possible. The sash should protect the head and upper body in case of an explosion. (Safety goggles are required.)
- Do not place your head in the hood when contaminants are being generated.
- Do not use the fume hood as a waste disposal unit except for very small amounts of volatile chemicals.
- Do not store chemicals or apparatuses in the hood.
- Keep the slots in the hood baffle (air intake) free from obstructions.
- Keep the laboratory door closed unless indicated from the manufacturer.
- Remove the sash or panels only when necessary for apparatus setup. Do not operate until sash has been replaced.

- Do not place electrical receptacles or other sources that may produce a spark in the fume hood when using flammable chemicals or when gases may be present.
- The hood's sash should be marked for appropriate closure point when it is necessary to partially close the sash during an operation.
- The sash should be closed when the hood's exhaust system is not operating.
- Provide regular maintenance on the hood's exhaust system. Use static pressure gauges on the hood throat and across filters in the exhaust system to ensure proper exhaust flow.

Eyewashes

The first response prior to medical treatment, for a student or teacher who has hazardous material in the eye, is flushing with water to dilute chemicals, wash out debris, or irrigate the eyes. It is very important that the eyelids are held open and the eyeballs rolled so water can flow on all surfaces and in the folds surrounding the eyeballs. **Note:** Squeeze bottles are not sufficient and should not be used as eyewashes in any science laboratory.

An eyewash that can wash both eyes simultaneously should be located in every science laboratory, classroom, and preparation room where hazardous chemicals are used. To ensure that the eyewash station in your science facility will meet safety requirements, it should

- be located no more than 10 seconds (25 feet) from any student workstation.
- comply (one eyewash) with ADA regulations on accessibility.
- be provided sufficient water pressure to operate correctly.
- wash both eyes simultaneously.
- supply an instant flow of recirculated tempered water continuously for at least 15 minutes.
- have a water control valve that remains on, allowing the user to use both hands.
- be clearly marked and unobstructed for immediate use.

Note: Eyewashes should be flushed for 5 minutes once a week to remove any harmful contaminant that may form or grow in the eyewash.

Copyright © Glencoe/McGraw-Hill, a division of the McGraw-Hill Companies, Inc.

Chemical Safety and Disposal, *continued*

Safety Showers

A safety shower should be found in any laboratory where hazardous chemicals are used. Safety showers

- must meet the standards for height, spray pattern, tepid water temperature, and water flow of 20 gallons per minute at 30 PSI.
- should have a control valve that can remain on without requiring the use of the operator's hands.
- should be located no more than 50 feet or 10 seconds away from any student workstation.
- should be marked with a highly visible sign for each safety shower.
- should be large enough to accommodate the injured person and a teacher assisting with the emergency.
- should have a fixed valve handle or a chain with a large ring that can be pulled down to start the flow of water.
- must have sufficient water flow and pressure to function properly for immediate use.
- should be flushed once a week to eliminate contamination and check for proper working conditions.

Tepid water should not exceed the temperature of a person's eyeball (approximately 85°F) on combination eyewash/shower systems. Mixing valves for tepid water to eyewashes or eyewash/shower systems should have a minimum flow of 2 gallons per minute and a maximum flow of 60 gallons per minute.

Ventilation

A well-maintained ventilation system is an important contributor to a healthy environment in science classrooms and laboratories. According to the *NSTA Guide to School Science Facilities*, "Forced ventilation at a minimum rate of four changes of air per hour should be provided for science laboratories, and continuous ventilation at six changes per hour for chemical storage rooms. Assuming that there is a fume hood in each preparation room, four changes per hour is adequate. All exhausts should be vented to the outside of the building, not recirculated in the building's ventilation system.

Chemical storage rooms need systems that vent directly outside, usually to the roof, and away from fresh-air intake pipes. Stage cabinets for flammables should not be ventilated to the outside.

Every science room should be equipped with exhaust fans designed for rapid venting of smoke or bad odors created by an investigation.

Material Safety Data Sheets

Every chemical manufacturer is required by law to supply a recent Material Safety Data Sheet (MSDS) with each chemical it produces. These should be sent with each chemical that is purchased by a school or school district. If MSDS forms are not available, request them from the chemical manufacturer. Every teacher needs to know and understand the information on an MSDS. The following information should be listed on MSDS forms for science teachers.

- Product identification
- Hazardous components
- Physical data
- Fire and explosion hazards
- Health hazards
- Fire and explosion data
- Spill and disposal procedures
- Protective equipment
- Storage and handling procedures
- Transportation data and additional information

Chemical Storage

Safe chemical storage is based on the chemical properties of the substances that are to be stored. The hazards of the chemicals are closely associated with their chemical and physical properties. Proper storage of chemicals should follow these guidelines.

1. The chemicals must be properly labeled with the identity of the contents, hazards, and manufacturer's name and address.

2. The chemicals must be stored in compatible families.

3. The chemical storage room should be located so that people in the building or damage to the building will be minimal if an explosion or a fire was to occur.

4. The chemical storeroom must have two exits and doors that lock.
5. The doors should be labeled "Authorized Personnel Only" or "Hazardous Materials."
6. The storage room must have continuous forced air ventilation that is vented to the outside away from air intakes.
7. Storage cabinets and shelves must be resistant to corrosion.
8. Chemicals must be stored in upright position and no more than two or three containers deep.
9. Shelves may be equipped with a lip to prevent chemicals from being jarred off the shelf.
10. Corrosives (acids and bases) should be stored in an approved corrosive cabinet.
11. Flammables should be stored in an approved flammable cabinet.
12. Chemicals should not be stored above eye level and never stored on the floor.
13. Water-reactive chemicals (metals) should be stored where they will remain dry.
14. Proper safety equipment must be clearly marked inside the storeroom.
    - ABC fire extinguisher
    - Safety goggles
    - Fire blanket
    - Spill kit
    - First-aid kit
15. The room must be adequately lighted.
16. Smoke detectors should be present.
17. An ongoing chemical inventory should be maintained.

Chemical Disposal

There are several important steps that should be taken prior to proceeding with chemical disposal. First, determine how many chemicals are designated for disposal. Remove

- out-of-date or contaminated chemicals.
- chemicals without legible labels.
- chemicals that are too hazardous for student use.

Then, make arrangements with an appropriate disposal company.

Options for Proper Chemical Disposal

Contact commercial chemical disposal companies in your area. Many waste disposal companies recycle chemicals and resell them. Other options may be available by contacting

- other schools in your area and combine quantities for disposal.
- industries in the area for assistance in disposal.
- institutions of higher education. They may allow you to use their system of disposal.
- the Natural Resources Conservation Commission in your state.

Disposal of Liquid Waste

A frequent question from chemistry teachers is about which liquids may safely be disposed of in the sanitary drains. First, the teacher must be certain that the sewer flows to a wastewater treatment plant and not to a stream or other natural waterway. Second, any substance from a laboratory should be flushed with at least 100 times its own volume of tap water. Third, disposal methods should be checked with local authorities because local regulations are often more stringent than federal requirements. The book, *Prudent Practices in the Laboratory*, published by the National Research Council, Washington, DC: National Academy Press, 1995, lists many substances that can be disposed of in the sanitary drain.

Some positive and negative ions from the *Prudent Practices* lists are given in the table shown on the next page. Note that it is important that both the positive and negative ion of a salt be listed in order for its drain disposal to be considered safe. Also note that although hydrogen and hydroxide ions are listed, acids and bases should be neutralized before disposal. A good rule of thumb is that nothing of pH less than 3 or greater than 8 should be discarded without neutralizing it first.

Positive Ions	Negative Ions
aluminum	borate
ammonium	bromide
bismuth	carbonate
calcium	chloride
copper	hydrogen sulfate
hydrogen	hydroxide
iron	iodide
lithium	nitrate
magnesium	phosphate
potassium	sulfate
sodium	sulfite
strontium	tetraborate
tin	thiocyanate
titanium	
zinc	

Disposal of Organic Waste

Of the organic compounds most often found in high school laboratories, the following can be disposed of in the drain: methanol, ethanol, propanols, butanols, pentanols, ethylene, glycol, glycerol, sugars, formaldehyde, formic acid, acetic acid, oxalic acid, sodium and potassium salts of carboxylic acids, esters with fewer than five carbon atoms, and acetone. More extensive lists can be found in *Prudent Practices.*

Disposal of Other Waste

Other chemicals can be properly treated and disposed of in one of the following ways.

- Treat waste chemically to convert it to a form that is drain-disposable. A good example is the iodate ion, which is too strong an oxidizing agent to be disposed of untreated. However, it is readily reduced to iodide (disposable) by acidified sodium hydrogen sulfite. Many procedures for processing laboratory waste to a discardable form can be found in *Prudent Practices.*

- Recycle waste. A good example is the recovery of valuable metals such as mercury and silver. Solvents can be recycled through distillation.

- If a waste cannot be recycled or processed to disposable form, then it must be packed and shipped by a Department of Transportation-approved shipper to a landfill designated to receive chemical and hazardous waste.

Numerous processes are described in *Prudent Practices* for reducing both the bulk and hazard of wastes. An example is the reduction of chromate and dichromate waste solutions to chromium(III) solutions, which are then made basic. The chromium(III) oxide precipitate is filtered off, dried, and crushed, resulting in significant savings. As hazardous wastes are accumulated awaiting shipment, it is important to observe the proper storage procedures for separating incompatible substances.

Microscale Chemistry

Microscale science techniques may appear out of place in a discussion of laboratory safety. Quite the contrary, microscale techniques offer a pedagogically sound approach to science laboratory investigations and provide simple solutions to many safety issues.

Major concepts emphasized in laboratory instruction have shifted from a simple reduction in amounts of chemicals used to a reeducation approach. The primary construct put forth by advocates of microscale chemistry is to instill in educators and students "If you don't need that much, then don't use it." The purpose is to move away from the throwaway mentality in our society. One way to express to students that the prevention of environmental pollution begins at the source is to reduce the amount of materials being "wasted" while teaching them basic science concepts.

Hazardous waste management is a problem confronting all educational institutions. Schools are finding it increasingly difficult to fund the disposal of hazardous waste while attempting to maintain a hands-on chemical learning environment. Microscale experiments make it possible to promote critical thinking skills while addressing major safety issues for a safe learning environment. Advantages of incorporating microscale/small scale chemistry into the learning environment include the

- reduction in the cost of chemicals.
- reduction of possible fire and explosion danger.
- reduction of chemical waste disposal costs.
- introduction of experiments where chemicals once thought to be too expensive or hazardous can be made available with the reduced amounts.

- recycling products for future experiments (plan ahead and use it again).
- introduction of less expensive glassware.
- reduction of exposure to toxic materials.

Safety Advantages

Using microscale techniques means that dispensing liquids from plastic dropper bottles greatly reduces many spills. Accidental glass container breakage and fire hazards are eliminated, and air quality is improved due to smaller amounts of escaping vapor. Although some liquid is lost due to vaporization during both techniques, the microscale technique reduces hazardous organic chemicals that must be recovered and disposed of properly. In addition, this technique represents a responsible step in reducing environmental pollutants. In the science storeroom, chemicals in smaller containers (approximately 10% of the size used in macroscale) reduce the need for storage space.

Chemical Spills

If a chemical spill occurs in the laboratory or preparatory room, quick action by the teacher can reduce the possibility of injury to a student or teacher. A chemical spill such as a liter bottle of hydrochloric acid breaking in the laboratory is considered a major spill. The teacher should

- immediately evacuate all students through the exits farthest from the spill. Fumes from a chemical spill can cause severe damage to the body.

- immediately assist any person splashed with the chemical to the safety shower.
- turn on the emergency exhaust fan.
- contain the spill wearing proper protective clothing. Do not allow the spill to trap you.
- call for help. The school safety plan should contain agencies or departments in your community that will assist in containment and removal of the chemical.

Spill-Control Materials

There are many types of commercial materials that have been developed for containment and removal of chemical spills. They range from absorbent pads that quickly absorb chemicals in a liquid state, porous bags filled with an amorphous silicate, to materials that neutralize an acid or a caustic spill.

What is typically found in public schools is a plastic 5-gallon bucket filled with dry sand, vermiculite, or dry clay materials. These do nothing to neutralize an acid or a base, but they absorb the liquid or contain it in a small area. The disadvantage of using sand is that it is heavy and difficult to transport.

Once the chemical has been contained and neutralized, use clean-up equipment that is made of plastic or polypropylene so that the equipment doesn't react with any of the chemical that remains. The contaminated material is to be placed in plastic bags or containers and marked appropriately. The custodial staff should be informed of the material so that it can be disposed of properly.

List of Materials per Lab

(quantities needed for a class of 30 students)

Lab	Equipment	Expendables	Chemical Supplies
1	100-mL beakers (15) 25-mL graduated cylinders (15) 24-well microplates (15) balances (15) mortar and pestles (15) spatulas (15) thin-stem pipettes (15)	candy white paper (15 sheets)	
2	50-mL graduated cylinders (15) balances (15) *CRC Handbook of Chemistry and Physics* (optional)	paper towel (1 roll)	metal samples, including lead, iron, aluminum, copper (4 of each) water
3	mortar and pestles (15) 24-well microplates (15) thin-stem pipettes (15) spatulas (15)	toothpicks (30) white paper (15 sheets)	aspirin tablets (15 old, 15 new) isopropyl alcohol (2-propanol) (150 mL) iron(III) nitrate solution (40 mL) iodine solution (40 mL)
4	96-well microplates (45) thin-stem pipettes (105)	black construction paper (15 sheets) 96-well templates toothpicks (45)	Solutions of: $Mg(NO_3)_2$, $Ca(NO_3)_2$, $Sr(NO_3)_2$, $Ba(NO_3)_2$, Na_2SO_4, $Na_2C_2O_4$, Na_2CO_3 (200 mL of each) distilled water
5	96-well microplates (15) thin-stem pipettes (15)	96-well templates (15) toothpicks (40)	Solutions of: $0.1M$ KNO_3, $0.1M$ $Ca(NO_3)_2$, $0.1M$ NH_4VO_3, $0.1M$ $Cr(NO_3)_3$, $0.1M$ $Mn(NO_3)_2$, $0.1M$ $Fe(NO_3)_3$, $0.1M$ $Co(NO_3)_2$, $0.1M$ $Ni(NO_3)_2$, $0.1M$ $Cu(NO_3)_2$, $0.1M$ $Zn(NO_3)_2$, $6M$ NH_3, $1M$ $KSCN$, $6M$ HCl (100 mL of each)
6		round balloons (60) pear-shaped balloons (90) clear adhesive tape (3 rolls) string (15 m)	
7	24-well microplates (15) pipettes (135)		Solutions of: $1.0M$ $BaCl_2$, $1.0M$ $CuSO_4$, $1.0M$ $FeCl_3$, $1.0M$ KI, $1.0M$ $NaCl$, $1.0M$ $NaCO_3$, $1.0M$ $NaOH$, $1.0M$ Na_2SO_4, $1.0M$ $Pb(NO_3)_2$ (75 mL of each)

Lab	Equipment	Expendables	Chemical Supplies
8	50-mL beakers (15) 10-mL graduated cylinders (15) metric rulers (15) iron rings (15) Pasteur pipettes with suction bulb (15) large watch glasses (15) ring stands (15) small test tubes (30) test-tube racks (15) scoops (15)		stearic acid solution (0.05 g) cyclohexane (500 mL) lycopodium powder, or talcum powder (30 g) distilled water
9	100-mL beakers (15) thermometers (15) capillary tubes, sealed at one end (45) small test tubes (45) thin-stem pipettes (15) hot plates (15) ring stands (15) thermometer clamps (15) rubber bands (15) glass stirring rods (15)		acetone (60 mL) ethanol (60 mL) 1-propanol (60 mL)
10	Boyle's law apparatus (15) balances (15) metric rulers (15)	carpet thread (1.5 m)	flat objects that can be stacked (mass of objects is 500–550 g) (60)
11	400-mL beakers (15) 250-mL beakers (15) 100-mL beakers (15) thin-stem pipettes (15) wide-stem pipettes (15) scissors (15) metric rulers (15) stopwatches (15) fume hood		concentrated ammonia solution (75 mL) crushed ice
12	400-mL beakers (30) 100-mL graduated cylinders (15) large test tubes (45) boiling chips scissors (15) balances (15) hot plates (15) thermometers (15) test-tube racks (15)	plastic-foam cups (30)	small samples of metal: aluminum, iron, and lead (15 of each)

Lab	Equipment	Expendables	Chemical Supplies
13	24-well microplate (15) thin-stem pipettes (30) thermometers (15) scissors (15)	toothpicks (1 box)	NH_4Cl (30 g) $NaHCO_3$ (30 g) 6M HCl (15 mL) distilled water
14	24-well microplate with deep wells (15) droppers (45) stopwatch or clock with second hand (15)	white paper (15 sheets) toothpicks (45)	$2.0 \times 10^{-4}M$ crystal violet solution (30 mL) 1.0M NaOH solution (75 mL) distilled water
15	10-mL graduated cylinders (15) grease pencils (15) droppers (30) medium test tubes (105) stirring rods (15) test-tube racks (15)		0.1M $Fe(NO_3)_3$ (60 mL) 0.1M KSCN (60 mL) 1.0M NaOH (30 mL) 0.1M $AgNO_3$ (6 mL) $Fe(NO_3)_3$ (7.5 g) NH_4SCN (7.5 g) KCl (7.5 g) distilled water
16	24-well microplates (15) thin-stem pipettes (90)	white paper (15 sheets)	0.200M $Fe(NO_3)_3$ (400 mL) 0.6M HNO_3 (200 mL) $2.00 \times 10^{-3}M$ KSCN (200 mL)
17	24-well microplates (15) thin-stem pipettes (180)	pH papers (15 vials of various pH ranges)	0.100M boric acid, H_3BO_3 (400 mL) 0.100M citric acid, $H_3C_6H_5O_7$ (400 mL) 0.100M hydrogen peroxide, H_2O_2 (400 mL) 0.100M permanganic acid, $HMnO_4$ (400 mL) distilled water
18	10-mL graduated cylinders (15) 50-mL beakers (15) mortar and pestles (15) thin-stem pipettes (45) stirring rods (15)	pH papers (15 vials) plastic spoons (15)	0.1M NaOH (150 mL) unbuffered aspirin tablets (15) buffered aspirin tablets (15) distilled water

Lab	Equipment	Expendables	Chemical Supplies
19	100-mL beakers (15) 10-mL graduated cylinders (15) micropipettes (30) test tubes (30) thermometers (30) test-tube holders (30) test-tube racks (30) hot plates (30) stirring rods (30)	grease pencils (30)	$KMnO_4$ solution (150 mL) $1.0M$ solution of H_2SO_4 (45 mL) $Na_2C_2O_4$ (1.5 g) distilled water
20	micropipettes (30) small test tubes (45) scissors (15) scoops (15) stirring rods (15) test-tube racks (15) light source	green leaves (15) plastic weighing cups (15)	0.2% sodium hydrogen carbonate ($NaHCO_3$) solution (30 mL) methylene blue indicator solution (15 mL) distilled water

Safety in the Laboratory

The activities in *Chemistry: Matter and Change* are designed to minimize dangers in the laboratory. Careful planning and preparation as well as being aware of hazards can keep accidents to a minimum. Practice good laboratory housekeeping and management by observing these guidelines.

Personal Protection

The use of personal protection equipment is required when potentially hazardous material is present. Personal protection equipment includes eyewear, protective gloves, and laboratory aprons and coats.

Eyewear

Safety goggles are required for science laboratory and field activities involving any hazardous chemical, which could damage the eye if splashed or rubbed into the eye. Goggles provide eye protection from fine dusts, liquids, splashes, mists, and sprays. They also prevent splashes and sprays from body fluids or dangerous chemicals.

Safety goggles should be large enough to protect and form a seal around the eyes. If not able to seal, goggles should contain side shields to prevent contamination to the eyes.

Eyewear should meet the ANSI Standard Z87.1- *Practice for Occupational and Educational Eye and Face Protection*. Eyewear meeting this standard will bear markings such as "Z87.1" on the frames, and the lens will be marked with the manufacturer's trademark.

Eye protection may also be provided with safety glasses. Safety glasses with side shields will not provide adequate protection from chemical splashes. They are designed primarily to protect the eyes from flying objects.

Protective Gloves

Gloves protect hands from heat, absorb perspiration, provide a shield from corrosive chemicals and body fluids, and prevent the transmission of microorganisms from person to person. Always check gloves to be sure that there are no tears, punctures, or holes. When removing gloves, peel the gloves off your hand, starting at the wrists and working toward the fingers. Keep the working surface of the gloves from contact with the skin during removal.

PROTECTIVE GLOVES AND THEIR FUNCTION	
GLOVE TYPE	**FUNCTION**
Plastic	Protects against light corrosives and irritants.
Latex	Provides protection against biological materials. Should be changed as soon as they are soiled. *Note: Some people may have an allergic reaction to latex, which can lead to serious medical problems.*
Natural Rubber	Protects against electric shock and light corrosive material.
Neoprene	Use when working with solvents, oils, or light corrosive material.
Cotton	Absorbs perspiration. Wear under latex gloves.
Asbestos	Insulates against heat. *Note: Asbestos gloves are labeled with a warning about the danger of cancer. Asbestos is a known carcinogen.*

Laboratory Aprons and Coats

Laboratory aprons and coats are designed to protect clothing and skin from splashed and spilled chemicals and biological materials. They should fit the wearer properly to provide maximum protection. A laboratory coat or apron should be worn at all times in the laboratory.

Aprons are usually listed as "bib type," which are suitable for laboratory use. Aprons should be worn over clothing that covers the arms and body. Laboratory coats are usually fire retardant and made of cotton or paper. They are good for protection against flying objects, sharp or rough edges, splashes and spills, and fire.

Fire Protection

Fire is one of the most frequent mishaps in the science laboratory. The first line of defense from a fire is fire prevention. Effective fire prevention centers on thorough understanding of combustion and the required ingredients. As long as air is present, oxygen will be available for combustion to take place. The areas where prevention measures are best exercised are the fuel and ignition sources.

Fires are classified by the chemical properties of the fuel. The basic classifications are grouped as follows.

- Class A – Ordinary combustible (i.e., paper, wood)
- Class B – Organic solvents (i.e., acetone, alcohols, ethers)
- Class C – Electrical wiring or static charges
- Class D – Active metals (i.e., sodium, potassium, magnesium)

These symbols are accepted for the different classifications of fire. They are applied to fire extinguishers and extinguisher locations to indicate their suitability in extinguishing the different types of fires.

The following precautions should be taken to prevent fires from occurring in the science classroom, laboratory, storage room, and preparation area.

- Be aware of ignition sources in your laboratory area (open flames, heat, and electrical equipment).
- Purchase and store flammable reagents in the smallest quantities possible.
- Do not store flammable liquids in standard refrigerators (an explosion-proof refrigerator should be used).
- Store flammable liquids in appropriate safety cabinets and/or safety cans.
- Do not store incompatible reagents together (e.g., acids with flammables).
- Do not store ethers for extended periods of time as explosive peroxides can form.
- Make sure that all electrical cords are in good condition. All electrical outlets should be grounded and should accommodate a 3-pronged plug.

Each science classroom, laboratory, storage room, and preparation area should have a fire blanket and an appropriate fire extinguisher.

Fire Extinguishers

In most school environments, handheld, portable fire extinguishers are the first fire-extinguishing agent used. Therefore, a multipurpose ABC fire extinguisher must be located in each science classroom, laboratory, storage room, and preparation area. Extinguishers must be

- located to be easily seen and the area around them kept clear.
- inspected on a regular basis.
- used by well-trained teachers and students.

Fire extinguishers are labeled in accordance with NFPA standards.

Fire Blankets

Actual fire control revolves around proper types of control devices such as a fire blanket. Fire blankets are made of specially treated fabric and should be located at strategic areas for all science laboratories where hazardous chemicals are stored and used. Fire blankets can be used if one is unable to reach the safety shower.

Electrical Protection

Electrical safety needs must be considered for all new, old, and renovated science classrooms, laboratories, storage rooms, and preparation areas. The emphasis of electrical safety should be on prevention. Minimum considerations for electrical safety include the following.

- Ground-fault interrupters (GFI) should be installed to protect against major shock and electrical fires by preventing short circuits.
- All outlets must be grounded to prevent electrical accidents. Sufficient outlets should be provided to eliminate the need for extension cords. If floor boxes are used, they should not be located near water sources or areas where water is used.
- Surge protectors should be used to protect computers and other electronic devices from power surges.

Safety in the Laboratory, *continued*

- Emergency shut-off controls (electricity, gas, and water) should be located in an area that is not easily accessible to students.
- Circuits should not be overloaded.
- Use only spark-free refrigeration in laboratories, storage rooms, and preparation areas for storage of flammable chemicals.
- Avoid the use of extension cords.
- Wiring should not have frayed or bare areas.

In developing the school's safety program, include provisions for handling electrical emergencies. All teachers of science should know where the master electrical cutoff switch and the control box are located, and how to operate both of these. Before an activity is conducted that requires the use of an electrical device, the teacher and students must be familiar with its operation and safety features.

Safety in the Laboratory material used with permission from Texas Safety Standards, produced by the Texas Education Agency.

24-Well Microplate

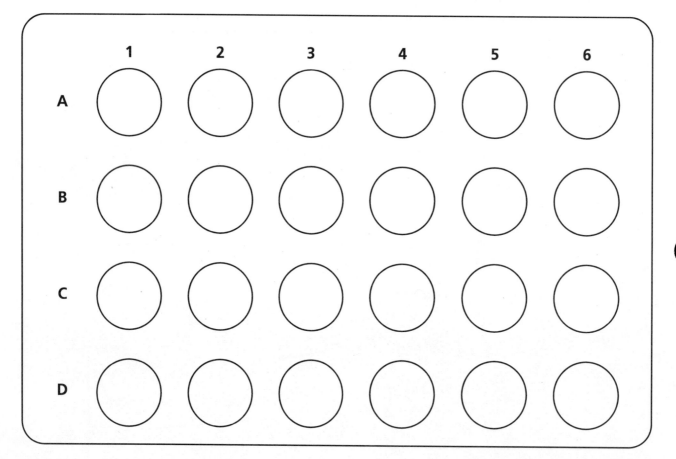

24-Well Microplate Template

	A	B	C	D
1				
2				
3				
4				
5				
6				

96-Well Microplate

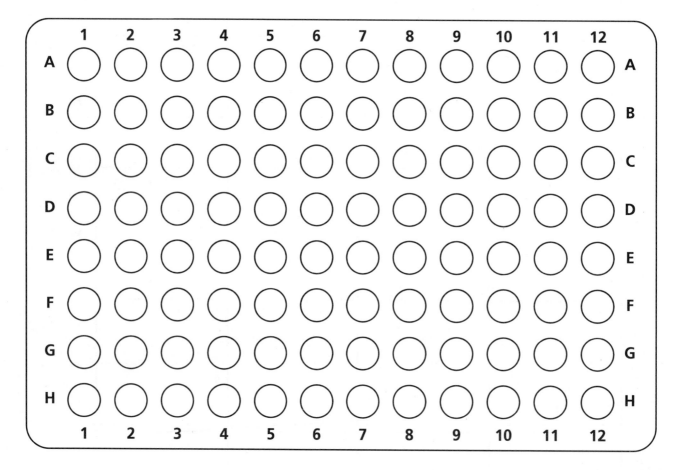

Small-Scale Laboratory Manual

96-Well Microplate Template

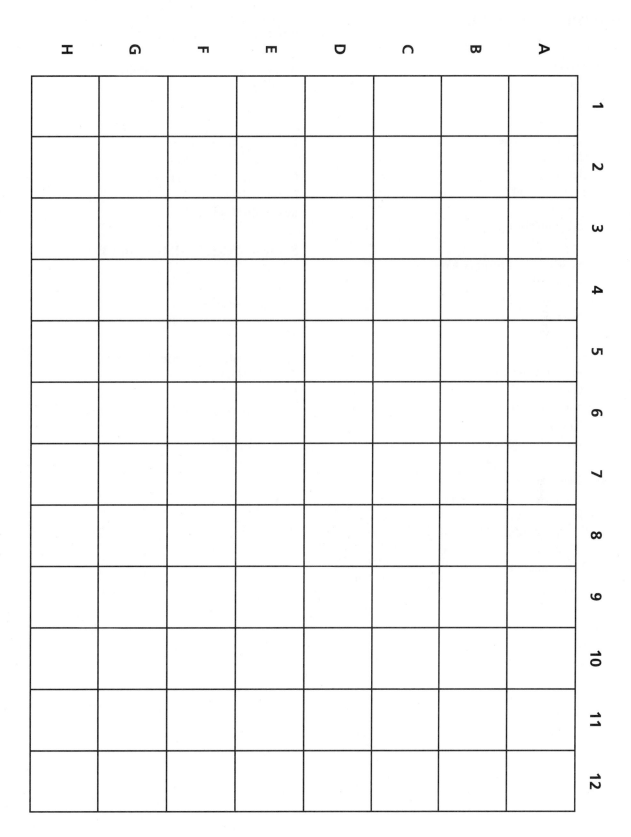

Suppliers

Equipment Suppliers

American Science & Surplus
3605 Howard St.
Skokie, IL 60076
(800) 934-0722

Bio-Rad Laboratories
2000 Alfred Nobel Dr.
Life Science Group
Hercules, CA 94547
(800) 876-3425
ron_mardigian@bio-rad.com

Carolina Biological Supply Co.
2700 York Road
Burlington, NC 27215
(800) 334-5551
www.carolina.com

Edmund Scientific Company
101 E. Gloucester Pike
Barrington, NJ 08007
(609) 547-3488
scientifics@edsci.com

Fisher Science Education
Educational Materials Division
485 S. Frontage Rd.
Burr Ridge, IL 60521
(800) 955-1177
www.fisheredu.com

Nasco Science
901 Janesville Avenue
P.O. Box 901
Fort Atkinson, WI 53538-0901
(800) 558-9595
www.nascofa.com

Nebraska Scientific
3823 Leavenworth St.
Omaha, NE 68105-1180
(800) 228-7117
nescientif@aol.com

Sargent-Welch/VWR Scientific Products
P.O. Box 5229
Buffalo Grove, IL 60089-5229
(800) SAR-GENT
www.SargentWelch.com

Ward's Natural Science Est.
5100 W. Henrietta Road
P.O. Box 92912
Rochester, NY 14692-9012
(800) 962-2660
www.wardsci.com

Glencoe

CHEMISTRY
MATTER AND CHANGE

Small-Scale Laboratory Manual

Student Edition

Glencoe
McGraw-Hill

New York, New York   Columbus, Ohio   Woodland Hills, California   Peoria, Illinois

A GLENCOE PROGRAM

Glencoe
CHEMISTRY
MATTER AND CHANGE

Hands-On Learning:
Laboratory Manual, SE/TE
Forensics Laboratory Manual, SE/TE
CBL Laboratory Manual, SE/TE
Small-Scale Laboratory Manual, SE/TE
ChemLab and MiniLab Worksheets

Review/Reinforcement:
Study Guide for Content Mastery, SE/TE
Solving Problems: A Chemistry Handbook
Reviewing Chemistry
Guided Reading Audio Program

Applications and Enrichment:
Challenge Problems
Supplemental Problems

Assessment:
Chapter Assessment
MindJogger Videoquizzes (VHS/DVD)
Computer Test Bank, Windows/MacIntosh

Teacher Resources:
Lesson Plans
Block Scheduling Lesson Plans
Spanish Resources
Section Focus Transparencies and Masters
Math Skills Transparencies and Masters
Teaching Transparencies and Masters
Solutions Manual

Technology:
Chemistry Interactive CD-ROM
Vocabulary PuzzleMaker Software,
    Windows/MacIntosh
Glencoe Science Web site:
science.glencoe.com

Send all inquiries to:
Glencoe/McGraw-Hill
8787 Orion Place
Columbus, OH 43240-4027

ISBN 0-07-824528-1
Printed in the United States of America.
1 2 3 4 5 6 7 8 9 10 045 09 08 07 06 05 04 03 02 01

Contents

Laboratory Activities

To the Student

Chemistry is the science of matter, its properties, and changes. In your classroom work in chemistry, you will learn a great deal of the information that has been gathered by scientists about matter. But chemistry is not just information. It is also a process for finding out more about matter and its changes. Laboratory activities are the primary means that chemists use to learn more about matter. The activities in the *Small-Scale Laboratory Manual* require that you form and test hypotheses, measure and record data and observations, analyze those data, and draw conclusions based on those data and your knowledge of chemistry. These processes are the same as those used by professional chemists and all other scientists.

Small-Scale Laboratory Manual activities use the latest development in laboratory techniques—small-scale chemistry. In small-scale chemistry, you often use plastic pipettes and microplates instead of large glass beakers, flasks, and test tubes. You also use small amount of chemicals in reactions. Still, when working with small-scale chemistry, you should use the same care in obtaining data and making observations that you would use in large-scale laboratory activities. Likewise, you must observe the same safety precautions as for any chemistry experiment.

Organization of Activities

- **Introduction** Following the title and number of each activity, an introduction provides a background discussion about the problem you will study in the activity.
- **Problem** The problem to be studied in this activity is clearly stated.
- **Objectives** The objectives are statements of what you should accomplish by doing the investigation. Recheck this list when you have finished the activity.
- **Materials** The materials list shows the apparatus you need to have on hand for the activity.
- **Safety Precautions** Safety symbols and statements warn you of potential hazards in the laboratory. Before beginning any activity, refer to page vii to see what these symbols mean.
- **Pre-Lab** The questions in this section check your knowledge of important concepts needed to complete the activity successfully.
- **Procedure** The numbered steps of the procedure tell you how to carry out the activity and sometimes offer hints to help you be successful in the laboratory. Some activities have **CAUTION** statements in the procedure to alert you to hazardous substances or techniques.
- **Hypothesis** This section provides an opportunity for you to write down a hypothesis for this activity.
- **Data and Observations** This section presents a suggested table or form for collecting your laboratory data. Always record data and observations in an organized way as you do the activity.
- **Analyze and Conclude** The Analyze and Conclude section shows you how to perform the calculations necessary for you to analyze your data and reach conclusions. It provides questions to aid you in interpreting data and observations in order to reach an experimental result. You are also asked to form a scientific conclusion based on what you actually observed, not what "should have happened." An opportunity to analyze possible errors in the activity is also given.
- **Real-World Chemistry** The questions in this section ask you to apply what you have learned in the activity to other real-life situations. You may be asked to make additional conclusions or research a question related to the activity.

Small-Scale Laboratory Techniques

Small-scale chemistry uses smaller amounts of chemicals than do other chemistry methods. The hazards of glass have been minimized by the use of plastic labware. If a chemical reaction must be heated, hot water will provide the needed heat. Open flames or burners are seldom used in microchemistry techniques. By using small-scale chemistry, you will be able to do more experiments and have a safer environment in which to work.

Small-scale chemistry uses two basic tools.

The Microplate

The first is a sturdy plastic tray called a microplate. The tray has shallow wells arranged in rows (running across) and columns (running up and down). These wells are used instead of test tubes, flasks, and beakers. Some microplates have 96 wells; other microplates have 24 larger wells.

The Plastic Pipette

Small-scale chemistry uses a pipette made of a form of plastic that is soft and very flexible. The most useful property of the pipette is the fact that the stem can be stretched without heating into a thin tube. If the stem is stretched and then cut with scissors, the small tip will deliver a tiny drop of reagent. You may also use a pipette called a microtip pipette, which has been pre-stretched at the factory. It is not necessary to stretch a microtip pipette.

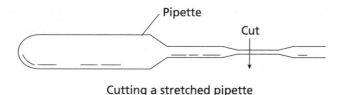

Cutting a stretched pipette

The pipette can be used over and over again simply by rinsing the stem and bulb between reagents. The plastic inside the pipette is non-wetting and does not hold water or solutions the way glass does.

The Microplate Template and Microplate Data Form

Your teacher can provide you with Microplate Templates and Microplate Data Forms whenever you carry out an activity that requires them.

To help you with your observations, place the Microplate Template beneath your 24-well or 96-well microplate. The template is marked with the correct number of wells, and each row and column is labeled to help guide you with your placement of chemicals from the micropipettes. The white paper background provided by the template allows you to observe color changes and precipitate formations with ease.

Use Microplate Data Forms to write down the chemicals used and to record your observations of the chemical reactions that occur in each well.

Waste Disposal

Discard all substances according to your teacher's instructions. All plastic small-scale chemistry equipment can be washed with distilled water for reuse.

Safety in the Laboratory

The chemistry laboratory is a place to experiment and learn. You must assume responsibility for your own personal safety and that of people working near you. Accidents are usually caused by carelessness, but you can help prevent them by closely following the instructions printed in this manual and those given to you by your teacher. The following are some safety rules to help guide you in protecting yourself and others from injury in a laboratory.

1. The chemistry laboratory is a place for serious work. Do not perform activities without your teacher's permission. **Never** work alone in the laboratory. Work only when your teacher is present.

2. Study your lab activity **before** you come to the lab. If you are in doubt about any procedures, ask your teacher for help.

3. Safety goggles and a laboratory apron must be worn whenever you work in the lab. Gloves should be worn whenever you use chemicals that cause irritations or can be absorbed through the skin.

4. Contact lenses should not be worn in the lab, even if goggles are worn. Lenses can absorb vapors and are difficult to remove in an emergency.

5. Long hair should be tied back to reduce the possibility of it catching fire.

6. Avoid wearing dangling jewelry or loose, draping clothing. The loose clothing may catch fire and either the clothing or jewelry could catch on chemical apparatus.

7. Wear shoes that cover the feet at all times. Bare feet or sandals are not permitted in the lab.

8. Know the location of the fire extinguisher, safety shower, eyewash, fire blanket, and first-aid kit. Know how to use the safety equipment provided for you.

9. Report any accident, injury, incorrect procedure, or damaged equipment immediately to your teacher.

10. Handle chemicals carefully. *Check the labels of all bottles **before** removing the contents.* Read the labels three times: before you pick up the container, when the container is in your hand, and when you put the bottle back.

11. Do **not** return unused chemicals to reagent bottles.

12. Do **not** take reagent bottles to your work area unless specifically instructed to do so. Use test tubes, paper, or beakers to obtain your chemicals.

Take only small amounts. It is easier to get more than to dispose of excess.

13. Do **not** insert droppers into reagent bottles. Pour a small amount of the chemical into a beaker.

14. **Never** taste any chemical substance. **Never** draw any chemicals into a pipette with your mouth. Eating, drinking, chewing gum, and smoking are prohibited in the laboratory.

15. If chemicals come into contact with your eyes or skin, flush the area immediately with large quantities of water. Immediately inform your teacher of the nature of the spill.

16. Keep combustible materials away from open flames. (Alcohol and acetone are combustible.)

17. Handle toxic and combustible gases only under the direction of your teacher. Use the fume hood when such materials are present.

18. When heating a substance in a test tube, be careful not to point the mouth of the tube at another person or yourself. Never look down the mouth of a test tube.

19. Use caution and the proper equipment when handling hot apparatus or glassware. Hot glass looks the same as cool glass.

20. Dispose of broken glass, unused chemicals, and products of reactions only as directed by your teacher.

21. Know the correct procedure for preparing acid solutions. *Always add the acid slowly to the water.*

22. Keep the balance area clean. Never weigh chemicals directly on the pan of the balance.

23. Do **not** heat graduated cylinders, burettes, or pipettes with a laboratory burner.

24. After completing an activity, clean and put away your equipment. Clean your work area. Make sure the gas and water are turned off. Wash your hands with soap and water before you leave the lab.

The *Chemistry: Matter and Change* program uses safety symbols to alert you and your students to possible laboratory dangers. These symbols are provided in the student text in Appendix B and are explained below. Be sure your students understand each symbol before they begin an activity that displays a symbol.

SAFETY SYMBOLS	HAZARD	EXAMPLES	PRECAUTION	REMEDY
DISPOSAL	Special disposal procedures need to be followed.	certain chemicals, living organisms	Do not dispose of these materials in the sink or trash can.	Dispose of wastes as directed by your teacher.
BIOLOGICAL	Organisms or other biological materials that might be harmful to humans	bacteria, fungi, blood, unpreserved tissues, plant materials	Avoid skin contact with these materials. Wear mask or gloves.	Notify your teacher if you suspect contact with material. Wash hands thoroughly.
EXTREME TEMPERATURE	Objects that can burn skin by being too cold or too hot	boiling liquids, hot plates, dry ice, liquid nitrogen	Use proper protection when handling.	Go to your teacher for first aid.
SHARP OBJECT	Use of tools or glassware that can easily puncture or slice skin	razor blades, pins, scalpels, pointed tools, dissecting probes, broken glass	Practice common-sense behavior and follow guidelines for use of the tool.	Go to your teacher for first aid.
FUME	Possible danger to respiratory tract from fumes	ammonia, acetone, nail polish remover, heated sulfur, moth balls	Make sure there is good ventilation. Never smell fumes directly. Wear a mask.	Leave foul area and notify your teacher immediately.
ELECTRICAL	Possible danger from electrical shock or burn	improper grounding, liquid spills, short circuits, exposed wires	Double-check setup with teacher. Check condition of wires and apparatus.	Do not attempt to fix electrical problems. Notify your teacher immediately.
IRRITANT	Substances that can irritate the skin or mucus membranes of the respiratory tract	pollen, moth balls, steel wool, fiber glass, potassium permanganate	Wear dust mask and gloves. Practice extra care when handling these materials.	Go to your teacher for first aid.
CHEMICAL	Chemicals that can react with and destroy tissue and other materials	bleaches such as hydrogen peroxide; acids such as sulfuric acid, hydrochloric acid; bases such as ammonia, sodium hydroxide	Wear goggles, gloves, and an apron.	Immediately flush the affected area with water and notify your teacher.
TOXIC	Substance may be poisonous if touched, inhaled, or swallowed	mercury, many metal compounds, iodine, poinsettia plant parts	Follow your teacher's instructions.	Always wash hands thoroughly after use. Go to your teacher for first aid.
OPEN FLAME	Open flame may ignite flammable chemicals, loose clothing, or hair	alcohol, kerosene, potassium permanganate, hair, clothing	Tie back hair. Avoid wearing loose clothing. Avoid open flames when using flammable chemicals. Be aware of locations of fire safety equipment.	Notify your teacher immediately. Use fire safety equipment if applicable.

Eye Safety
Proper eye protection should be worn at all times by anyone performing or observing science activities.

Clothing Protection
This symbol appears when substances could stain or burn clothing.

Animal Safety
This symbol appears when safety of animals and students must be ensured.

Radioactivity
This symbol appears when radioactive materials are used.

Small-Scale Laboratory Techniques

Use with Section 2.1

Nearly all experiments in chemistry involve making measurements of some sort. Measurements allow chemists to collect quantitative information about the phenomena they study, such as how much of a substance is present, what its temperature is, or how quickly it was produced. The equipment and techniques used to make scientific measurements vary with the type of information that is being collected.

Problem

What techniques are used to make a dilute solution of candy in water?

Objectives

- **Measure** the mass of a piece of candy.
- **Measure** the volume of a small amount of water.
- **Dissolve** the candy in the water.
- **Use** a pipette and a microplate to make serial dilutions of the candy-water solution.

Materials

100-mL beaker
25-mL graduated
  cylinder
24-well microplate
candy
balance

mortar and pestle
spatula
thin-stem pipette
sheet of white
  paper

Safety Precautions

- **Always wear safety goggles and a lab apron.**

Pre-Lab

1. What is the SI base unit for mass?
2. What quantity is measured in milliliters?
3. How many milliliters are in 1 liter? In 20 cubic centimeters?

Procedure

Part A: Measuring Mass

1. Slide all the riders on the balance as far to the left as they will go, as shown in **Figure A.** Check that the pointer swings freely along the scale.

2. With nothing on the balance pan, the pointer should swing an equal distance above and below the zero mark on the scale. If it does not, turn the adjustment screw until the swings above and below zero are equal.

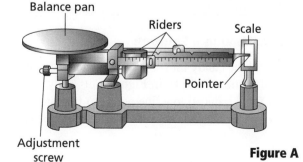

Figure A

3. Gently set the beaker on the balance pan. Notice that the pointer moves to the top of the scale.

4. Beginning with the largest rider on the top beam, move the riders to the right until the pointer again swings an equal distance above and below the zero mark. If the beams are notched, make sure each rider rests in a notch.

5. To find the mass of the beaker, add the masses indicated on the beam riders. Record the mass of the beaker to the nearest 0.1 g in **Data Table 1.**

6. Place one piece of candy in the beaker. Reposition the riders until the pointer again swings an equal distance above and below the zero mark. Record the mass of the beaker plus candy to the nearest 0.1 g in **Data Table 1.**

Figure B

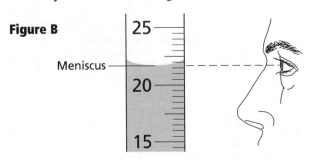

Meniscus

Part B: Measuring Volume

1. Pour about 20 mL of water into the graduated cylinder. As **Figure B** shows, the water in the cylinder has a curved surface, called a *meniscus*. To take a volume reading, view the bottom of the meniscus at eye level. Unless this position lines up exactly with a marking on the cylinder, you will need to estimate the distance between two markings.

2. The volume of water in the cylinder is measured by the closest marking on the side of the cylinder that lines up with the bottom of the meniscus. Record the volume to the nearest 0.1 mL in **Data Table 1.**

Part C: Making a Solution

1. Grind the candy into small pieces with the mortar and pestle, as shown in **Figure C.** (Candy should NOT be reduced to a fine powder.) Use the spatula to scrape the ground candy back into the beaker.

Figure C

2. If any candy remains in the mortar, pour some water from the graduated cylinder into the mortar. Grind the remaining candy in the mortar until it dissolves in the water. Pour this solution into the beaker.

3. Add the rest of the water to the beaker. Swirl the beaker until all of the pieces of candy are dissolved.

Part D: Making Serial Dilutions

1. Fill the graduated cylinder with water. Use the pipette to place 10 drops of water in the top left well of the microplate, as shown in **Figure D.** Notice that this well is labeled A1. **CAUTION: Never place the pipette in your mouth.**

2. Place 10 drops of the candy-water solution in well B1.

3. Transfer 1 drop of the candy-water solution from well B1 to well B2. Add 9 drops of water from the graduated cylinder to well B2. Well B2 now contains a diluted candy-water solution.

Figure D

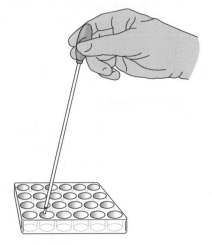

4. Place a sheet of white paper beneath the microplate. Compare the color of the contents of wells A1, B1, and B2.

5. Transfer 1 drop of the diluted candy-water solution to the next well in row B. Add 9 drops of water to that well. Compare the color of the new solution to that of the others.

6. Repeat step 5 until the most dilute solution appears completely colorless.

Cleanup and Disposal

1. Make sure your balance is left in the same condition as you found it and all riders are set to zero.

2. Return all lab equipment to its proper place.

3. Dispose of the candy-water solutions in the sink.

4. Wash your hands thoroughly with soap or detergent before you leave the lab.

Data and Observations

Data Table 1	
Mass of beaker (g)	
Mass of beaker + candy (g)	
Mass of candy (g)	
Volume of water (mL)	

Analyze and Conclude

1. **Measuring and Using Numbers** To find the mass of candy, subtract the mass of the beaker from the mass of the beaker + candy. Record the result in **Data Table 1.**

2. **Measuring and Using Numbers** Calculate the concentration of candy in the candy-water solution in well B1. (Hint: The answer should have units of g/mL.)

_____

_____

3. **Thinking Critically** Calculate the concentration of candy in the diluted candy-water solution in well B2. (Hint: Remember that you added 9 drops of water to 1 drop of the undiluted candy-water solution.)

_____

_____

4. **Measuring and Using Numbers** What was the concentration of candy in the most dilute solution you made (the one that appeared completely colorless)?

_____

_____

Real-World Chemistry

Ammonia solution is a household cleaner with many uses. To clean windows, you can prepare a diluted solution by mixing 1 tablespoon of ammonia solution with 1 quart of water. If the undiluted solution contains 10 percent ammonia, what percent of the diluted solution is ammonia? (Hint: 1 tablespoon = 15 mL, and 1 quart = 0.95 L)

LAB 2 SMALL-SCALE LABORATORY MANUAL

Comparing the Density of Metals

Use with Section 3.1

Different materials can be distinguished from one another because they have different properties. One property that is often used to identify unknown materials is density. Density is defined as the ratio of a material's mass to its volume. By measuring the mass and volume of a sample of material, you can obtain an important clue about the identity of the material.

Problem

Can you identify unknown metals by calculating their densities?

Objectives

- **Measure** the mass and volume of four metal samples.
- **Calculate** the density of each sample from these measurements.
- **Compare** the calculated densities with known densities of specific metals.
- **Identify** each metal sample.

Materials

metal samples
balance
50-mL graduated
   cylinder
water
paper towel
*CRC Handbook of
   Chemistry and
   Physics* (optional)

Safety Precautions

- **Always wear safety goggles and a lab apron.**

Pre-Lab

1. What is the formula to calculate density? What are the units for density?
2. Explain the difference between base units and derived units.
3. Is density measured in base units or derived units?
4. A sample of metal X has a mass of 85.6 g and a volume of 12.1 mL. What is the density of metal X?
5. A metal bar has a density of 19.3 g/mL and a mass of 50.0 kg. What is the volume of the bar?

Procedure

1. Select a metal sample from the materials table. Record the letter of the sample in **Data Table 1.**
2. Use the balance to measure the mass of the sample to the nearest 0.01 g. Record the mass in **Data Table 1.**
3. Fill the graduated cylinder half full of water. If there are air bubbles in the water, tap the outside of the cylinder with your finger to remove them. Record the volume of water to the nearest 0.1 mL.

LAB 2   **SMALL-SCALE LABORATORY MANUAL**

4. Tilt the cylinder and carefully insert the metal sample. Let the sample slide down the cylinder without splashing any water, as shown in **Figure A.** Make sure that the sample is completely under water and that there are no air bubbles. Then record the volume of water plus metal sample.

5. Repeat steps 1–4 for the other three metal samples.

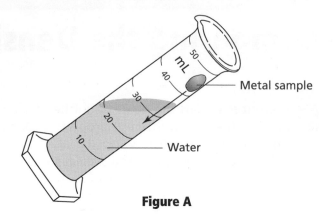

Figure A

Cleanup and Disposal

1. Dry the metal samples with a paper towel and return them to the materials table.

2. Make sure your balance is left in the same condition as you found it.

3. Return all lab equipment to its proper place, as directed by your teacher.

Data and Observations

Data Table 1					
Sample	Mass (g)	Volume of water (mL)	Volume of water + sample (mL)	Volume of sample (mL)	Density (g/mL)

1. To find the volume of each metal sample, subtract the volume of water from the volume of water + sample. Record the results in **Data Table 1.**

2. To calculate the density of each metal sample and record the results in **Data Table 1.**

Analyze and Conclude

1. **Acquiring and Analyzing Information** Look up the densities of the following metals: aluminum, copper, iron, lead, tin, tungsten, and zinc.

_____

_____

_____

_____

2. Drawing Conclusions Assume that the samples you tested may be any of the metals in question 1. Decide which metal each sample is likely to represent.

_____

_____

_____

_____

3. Applying Concepts If there were air bubbles in the water after you added a sample but not before, would that affect the density value you calculated for that sample? Explain.

_____

_____

_____

_____

_____

4. Thinking Critically Suppose you calculated the density of a metal sample to be 7 g/mL. Describe two ways you could determine whether the sample is made of tin or zinc.

_____

_____

_____

_____

_____

5. Error Analysis Find out from your teacher whether you correctly identified the samples. Compare the density you calculated for each sample with the accepted density of the metal it is made of. Calculate the percentage error if any. Explain possible sources of error in the lab.

_____

_____

_____

_____

_____

Name _____ Date _____ Class _____

LAB (2) SMALL-SCALE LABORATORY MANUAL

Real-World Chemistry

1. Body composition refers to the percentage of a person's body mass that is composed of lean tissue or fatty tissue. Lean tissue, which includes muscle and bone, is more dense than water. Fatty tissue is less dense than water. Would you expect a person who has 30 percent body fat to float higher or lower in the water than a person of the same mass who has 10 percent body fat? Explain.

2. Modern jet airplanes are built primarily out of aluminum and another metal, titanium, which has a density of 4.5 g/mL. Why do you think these metals are preferred over other metals, such as iron and lead?

3. Many metallic materials are alloys, or mixtures of two or more metals. For example, brass is an alloy of copper and zinc. How would you expect the density of brass to compare to the density of pure copper? Explain.

Copyright © Glencoe/McGraw-Hill, a division of the McGraw-Hill Companies, Inc.

8 *Chemistry: Matter and Change • Chapter 3* Small-Scale Laboratory Manual

Name _____ Date _____ Class _____

Separation of Aspirin

Use with
Section 3.3

One of the most frequently used pain relievers is acetylsalicylic acid, which is commonly called aspirin. An aspirin tablet contains more than aspirin, however. Manufacturers mix aspirin with starch, which keeps the tablets from falling apart and makes them large enough for easy handling. Furthermore, aspirin can break down into salicylic acid and acetic acid over time. Therefore, an aspirin tablet is a mixture of at least four substances: aspirin, starch, salicylic acid, and acetic acid.

Problem

How can you separate the substances in an aspirin tablet?

Objectives

- **Separate** an aspirin tablet into two phases.
- **Test** each phase for the presence of starch.
- **Test** one of the phases for the presence of salicylic acid.
- **Compare** the amount of salicylic acid in new and old aspirin tablets.

Materials

aspirin tablets
  (1 old, 1 new)
isopropyl alcohol
  (2-propanol)
iron(III) nitrate
  solution
iodine solution

mortar and pestle
24-well microplate
thin-stem pipette
spatula
toothpicks (2)
sheet of white
  paper

Safety Precautions

- **Always wear safety goggles, gloves, and a lab apron.**
- **Use care when handling all solutions.**

Pre-Lab

1. What is the difference between a heterogeneous mixture and a homogeneous mixture?

2. Classify the following mixtures as heterogeneous or homogeneous: salt and water, sand and water, nitrogen and oxygen in air.

3. Which technique—distillation, crystallization, or filtration—is most useful for separating a heterogeneous mixture composed of a solid and a liquid?

4. What technique is used to separate the substances in a solution based on differences in their boiling points?

5. Read the entire laboratory activity. Form a hypothesis about whether new or old aspirin tablets will contain more salicylic acid. Explain why. Record your hypothesis on page 10.

Procedure

1. Place a sheet of white paper beneath the 24-well microplate.

2. Grind an aspirin tablet from group A into small pieces with the mortar and pestle. Use the spatula to scrape the ground tablet into well A1 of the microplate.

3. Use the pipette to add 40 drops of isopropyl alcohol to well A1. Stir the mixture in well A1 with a toothpick.

4. Allow the solid material in well A1 to settle to the bottom of the well.

5. Use the pipette to remove the liquid from well A1. **CAUTION: Never place the pipette in your mouth.** Be careful not to draw up any of the solid material. The liquid consists of iso-propyl alcohol and any substances in the aspirin tablet that can dissolve in isopropyl alcohol. Place the liquid in well A2.

6. Repeat steps 3–5.

7. Transfer 10 drops of the liquid in well A2 to well A3.

8. Clean and dry the mortar and pestle.

9. Repeat steps 2–7 using an aspirin tablet from group B and wells B1–B3 of the microplate.

10. Add 1 drop of iodine solution to wells A1, A2, B1, and B2. Stir with a toothpick. Record what happens to the contents of each well in **Data Table 1.**

11. Add 1 drop of iron(III) nitrate solution to wells A3 and B3. Stir with a toothpick. Compare the color of the contents of these wells. Record your observations in **Data Table 1.**

Hypothesis

_____

_____

_____

Cleanup and Disposal

1. Dispose of all solutions as directed by your teacher.

2. Return all lab equipment to its proper place.

3. Wash your hands thoroughly with soap or detergent before you leave the lab.

Data and Observations

Data Table 1	
Well	**Observations**
A1	
A2	
A3	
B1	
B2	
B3	

Analyze and Conclude

1. **Applying Concepts** Does adding isopropyl alcohol to a crushed aspirin tablet make a homogeneous mixture or a heterogeneous mixture? Explain.

_____

_____

_____

2. **Observing and Inferring** Iodine solution turns blue or black when added to starch. Using this information, can you determine whether starch dissolves in isopropyl alcohol? Explain.

_____

_____

_____

3. **Observing and Inferring** Iron(III) nitrate solution turns violet when added to salicylic acid. Using this information, can you determine whether salicylic acid dissolves in iso-propyl alcohol? Explain.

_____

_____

_____

4. **Drawing a Conclusion** The more salicylic acid a solution contains, the darker the violet color that results when iron(III) nitrate solution is added. Using this information, compare the amount of salicylic acid in the aspirin tablets from group A and group B.

_____

_____

_____

5. **Drawing a Conclusion** Which tablet (A or B) was the old sample and which was the new sample?

_____

6. **Error Analysis** Find out from your teacher which group (A or B) contained old aspirin and which contained new aspirin. Then compare the results of this experiment with the predictions of your hypothesis. Explain possible reasons for any disagreement.

_____

_____

_____

LAB (3)

SMALL-SCALE LABORATORY MANUAL

Real-World Chemistry

1. Panning is a method for separating gold from the other materials with which it is often mixed. A person using this method fills a circular pan with gold-containing sand or gravel and swirls the pan under a gentle stream of water. Explain why the gold separates from the other materials under these conditions. (Hint: The density of gold is 19.3 g/mL, and the density of sand and gravel ranges from about 2.5 to 5.0 g/mL.)

2. Sodium chloride (table salt) is an essential nutrient for humans and other animals. It is also the major substance dissolved in seawater. Describe a simple method for separating sodium chloride from seawater.

3. Many communities have recycling programs for both aluminum cans and for cans made of iron. Some programs ask citizens to keep the two kinds of cans separate, while other programs do not. How might recyclers easily separate aluminum cans from cans made of iron, even if all of the cans are ground up and the pieces are thoroughly mixed together?

LAB **4** SMALL-SCALE LABORATORY MANUAL

Periodicity and the Properties of Elements

Use with Section 7.1

The periodic table of elements organizes the elements according to their atomic structures. The table is arranged in horizontal rows called periods and vertical columns called groups or families. Elements in the same group have similar chemical and physical properties. Thus, it is possible to predict many of the properties of an element by examining its position in the table. One such property is solubility. Solubility refers to the amount of a substance that can dissolve in a given amount of another substance. In this activity, you will demonstrate patterns of solubility.

Problem

How can you demonstrate patterns of solubility for compounds containing alkaline earth metals?

Objectives

- **Prepare** serial dilutions of solutions containing ions of alkaline earth metals.
- **Observe** precipitates that form when other chemicals are added to these solutions.
- **Recognize** patterns of solubility for compounds containing alkaline earth metals.

Materials

96-well
  microplates (3)
solutions of:
  $Mg(NO_3)_2$
  $Ca(NO_3)_2$
  $Sr(NO_3)_2$
  $Ba(NO_3)_2$
  Na_2SO_4
  $Na_2C_2O_4$
  Na_2CO_3

sheets of black
  construction
  paper (15)
96-well
  templates (3)
thin-stem
  pipettes (7)
toothpicks (45)
distilled water

Safety Precautions

- **Always wear safety goggles, gloves, and a lab apron.**
- **Use extra care when handling all solutions.**
- **Notify your teacher of any spills.**
- **Dispose of all solutions as directed by your teacher.**

Pre-Lab

1. Why do elements in the same group on the periodic table have similar properties?

2. Why don't elements in the same group have identical properties?

3. What is the relationship between reactivity and atomic number for metals in the same group?

4. Name the alkaline earth metals.

5. Read the entire laboratory activity. Form a hypothesis about the solubility of the compounds containing alkaline metals that you will test in this experiment. Record your hypothesis on page 14.

Procedure

1. Place a microplate on the construction paper with the lettered rows on the left.

2. Using a different pipette for each solution, place 10 drops of $Mg(NO_3)_2$ in well A1, 10 drops of $Ca(NO_3)_2$ in well B1, 10 drops of $Sr(NO_3)_2$ in well C1, and 10 drops of $Ba(NO_3)_2$ in well D1. **CAUTION: Never place the pipette in your mouth.**

3. Label all three templates to show the solutions that are in wells A1–D1. Title Template 1 "Precipitate Formed by Adding Na_2SO_4." Title Template 2 "Precipitate Formed by Adding $Na_2C_2O_4$." Title Template 3 "Precipitate Formed by Adding Na_2CO_3."

4. Add 5 drops of distilled water to each of wells A2–A12, B2–B12, C2–C12, and D2–D12.

5. Transfer 5 drops of the solution in well A1 to well A2. Mix thoroughly with a toothpick.

6. Continue transferring 5 drops from one well to the next through well A12, as diagrammed in **Figure A.**

7. Remove and discard 5 drops of the solution in well A12.

8. Using a different pipette for each row, repeat steps 5–7 for rows B, C, and D.

9. Add 5 drops of Na_2SO_4 to each well that contains a solution.

10. Examine each well for the presence of a precipitate (solid material at the bottom of the well). Indicate which wells contain a precipitate on Template 1.

11. Using a clean microplate, repeat steps 2–8. You may use the same pipettes you used before to transfer the solutions.

12. Add 5 drops of $Na_2C_2O_4$ to each well that contains a solution.

13. Examine each well for the presence of a precipitate. Indicate which wells contain a precipitate on Template 2.

14. Using a clean microplate, repeat steps 2–8. You may use the same pipettes you used before to transfer the solutions.

15. Add 5 drops of Na_2CO_3 to each well that contains a solution.

16. Examine each well for the presence of a precipitate. Indicate which wells contain a precipitate on Template 3.

Hypothesis

_____

_____

_____

Cleanup and Disposal

1. Dispose of all chemicals and solutions as directed by your teacher.

2. Return all lab equipment to its proper place.

3. Wash your hands thoroughly with soap or detergent before you leave the lab.

Data and Observations

Use your three templates to record your observations.

Figure A

Transfer 5 drops from one well to the next.

Discard 5 drops.

$Mg(NO_3)_2$

$Ca(NO_3)_2$

$Sr(NO_3)_2$

$Ba(NO_3)_2$

Copyright © Glencoe/McGraw-Hill, a division of the McGraw-Hill Companies, Inc.

Analyze and Conclude

1. **Measuring and Using Numbers** Explain how the concentration of alkaline earth metals (amount of metal ion per drop of solution) varied within each row of wells on the microplates.

_____

_____

2. **Collecting and Interpreting Data** Which alkaline earth metal(s) continued to form precipitates as the concentration became more dilute?

_____

_____

3. **Observing and Inferring** Which alkaline earth metal(s) did not form precipitates at any concentration?

_____

_____

4. **Drawing a Conclusion** Compounds with a lower solubility in water will form precipitates in wells with a lower concentration of metal ions. Use this information to describe the general pattern of solubility from magnesium to barium of compounds containing these metals.

_____

_____

5. **Error Analysis** Compare the results of this experiment with your hypothesis. Explain possible reasons for any disagreement.

_____

_____

_____

Real-World Chemistry

1. Water that contains high concentrations of magnesium or calcium ions along with carbonate (CO_3^-) ions can form deposits that may clog pipes. Based on your observations in this experiment, which metal ion—magnesium or calcium—do you think would contribute more to such deposits if both ions were present in equal concentrations? Explain your reasoning.

2. The alkaline earth metal beryllium exists naturally in compounds that almost always are mixed with aluminum compounds. Explain why it is difficult to isolate pure beryllium from these mixtures.

3. Physicians can treat some types of cancer by placing small amounts of a radioactive element in a sealed tube and inserting the tube in the cancerous tissue. Which of the alkaline earth metals could be used for this kind of treatment? Why?

LAB 5 SMALL-SCALE LABORATORY MANUAL

Properties of Transition Metals

Use with
Section 7.3

Like other metals, transition metals are malleable, lustrous, and good conductors of electricity. However, a variety of physical and chemical properties distinguish the transition metals from other metals. There also is considerable variability in the properties of the transition metals themselves. This variability results from differences in their electron configurations. In this activity, you will discover how transition metals differ chemically from other metals.

Problem
How can transition metals be distinguished chemically from other metals?

Objectives
- **Observe** the physical properties of ten metal ions in aqueous solution.
- **Observe** the results of mixing three chemicals with each of the solutions.
- **Compare** the chemical reactivity of transition metal ions with that of other metal ions.

Materials
96-well template
96-well microplate
thin-stem
  pipettes (15)
0.1M KNO$_3$
0.1M Ca(NO$_3$)$_2$
0.1M NH$_4$VO$_3$
0.1M Cr(NO$_3$)$_3$
0.1M Mn(NO$_3$)$_2$

0.1M Fe(NO$_3$)$_3$
0.1M Co(NO$_3$)$_2$
0.1M Ni(NO$_3$)$_2$
0.1M Cu(NO$_3$)$_2$
0.1M Zn(NO$_3$)$_2$
6M NH$_3$
1M KSCN
6M HCl
toothpicks (40)

Safety Precautions

- Always wear safety goggles, gloves, and a lab apron.
- Several solutions are poisonous. HCl is corrosive, and HCl and NH$_3$ will irritate the eyes, skin, and respiratory tract.
- Do not mix HCl and KSCN.
- Use extra care when handling all solutions.
- Notify your teacher of any spills.
- Do not dispose of wastes in the sink or trash can.
- Do not inhale vapors that are released.

Pre-Lab

1. What are transition metals?
2. Identify the metals in the ten solutions to be tested in this experiment (K, Ca, V, Cr, Mn, Fe, Co, Ni, Cu, and Zn).
3. Characterize the ten metals as group 1A metals, group 1B metals, or transition metals.
4. Read the entire laboratory activity. Form a hypothesis about which three metal ions will have

properties that are most different from those of the other metal ions. Explain why. Record your hypothesis on page 18.

Procedure

1. Label the 96-well template as shown in **Figure A.**
2. Set the microplate on top of the template with the lettered rows on the left.

Figure A

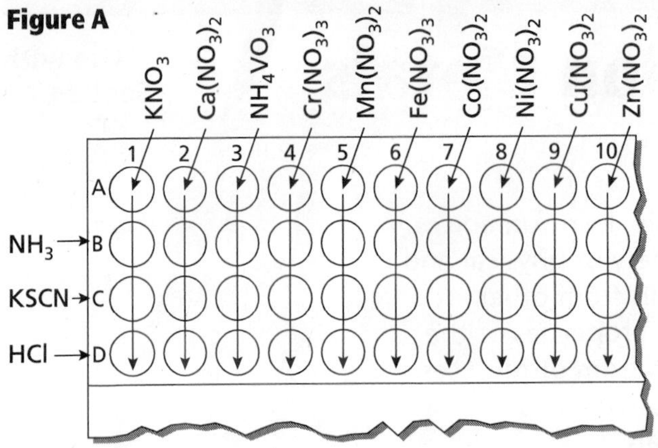

6. Add 5 drops of 1*M* KSCN to each of wells C1–C10. Stir the mixture in each well with a toothpick.

7. Add 5 drops of 6*M* HCl to each of wells D1–D10. Stir the mixture in each well with a toothpick.

Hypothesis

_____

_____

_____

_____

3. Use a pipette to place 5 drops of 0.1*M* KNO₃ in each of wells A1, B1, C1, and D1. **CAUTION: Never place the pipette in your mouth.**

4. Repeat step 3 for columns 2–10, using the solution assigned to each column on the template. For example, place 5 drops of 0.1*M* Ca(NO₃)₂ in each of wells A2, B2, C2, and D2.

5. Add 5 drops of 6*M* NH₃ to each of wells B1–B10. Stir the mixture in each well with a toothpick.

Cleanup and Disposal

1. Dispose of all chemicals and solutions as directed by your teacher.

2. Return all lab equipment to its proper place.

3. Wash your hands thoroughly before you leave the lab.

Data and Observations

Data Table 1				
Solution	Color of solution	Effect of adding other chemicals		
		NH₃	KSCN	HCl
KNO₃				
Ca(NO₃)₂				
NH₄VO₃				
Cr(NO₃)₃				
Mn(NO₃)₂				
Fe(NO₃)₃				
Co(NO₃)₂				
Ni(NO₃)₂				
Cu(NO₃)₂				
Zn(NO₃)₂				

1. Note the color of each solution in wells A1–A10. Record your observations in **Data Table 1.**

2. For each of wells B1–D10, note whether or not there was a chemical reaction. If there was a reaction that formed a precipitate, indicate the color of the precipitate in **Data Table 1.** If there was a color change without precipitate formation, indicate the new color. If there was no precipitate formation or color change, write *none* in **Data Table 1.**

Analyze and Conclude

1. **Observing and Inferring** Which mixtures caused precipitates to form?

   _____

   _____

   _____

2. **Thinking Critically** If no precipitate was formed when a chemical was added to a solution, does that mean a reaction did not occur? Explain.

   _____

   _____

   _____

3. **Observing and Inferring** Which solutions did not appear to react with any of the other chemicals?

   _____

   _____

   _____

4. **Error Analysis** Compare the results of this experiment with your hypothesis. Explain possible reasons for any disagreement.

   _____

   _____

   _____

   _____

   _____

Real-World Chemistry

1. Distillation is one method that can be used to separate a specific metal from a mixture of other elements. Distillation involves raising the temperature of a mixture until one of its components turns into a gas and then cooling the gas to recover that component as a liquid or solid. If there were a mixture containing all of the period 4 transition metals, which metal would be easiest to separate by distillation? Explain your reasoning. (Hint: Use a reference such as the *CRC Handbook of Chemistry and Physics* to find the boiling points of these metals.)

2. Cobalt chloride solution can be used as an "invisible ink." The solution leaves no detectable mark when it is applied to paper with a pen. However, heating the paper reveals the message written by the pen. Use your results in this experiment to predict the color of cobalt chloride ink on heated paper.

3. Many transition metals, including vanadium, chromium, manganese, and nickel, are included in alloys that are used to make products such as armor plate, safes, transmission gears, and high-speed metal-cutting tools. Explain why transition metals are used for such alloys.

LAB 6 **SMALL-SCALE LABORATORY MANUAL**

Modeling Molecular Shapes

A molecule consists of two or more atoms held together by covalent bonds. The shape of a molecule depends primarily on two factors: the number of covalent bonds formed by each atom, and the number of unshared (lone) pairs of electrons. These two factors are taken into account by the valence shell electron pair repulsion (VSEPR) model, which is used to predict molecular shapes. In this activity, you will model shapes of molecules.

Problem
How can you model the shapes of molecules in the laboratory?

Objectives
- **Construct** models of molecules by using inflated balloons.
- **Observe** how varying the number of covalent bonds and lone pairs of electrons affects molecular shape.

Materials
round balloons (4)
pear-shaped balloons (6)
clear adhesive tape
string

Safety Precautions

- Always wear safety goggles and a lab apron.
- Balloons containing latex may cause allergic reactions.

Pre-Lab

1. How does a covalent bond differ from an ionic bond?

2. How does the VSEPR model take into account the repulsion of electron pairs in predicting molecular shape?

3. What effect do lone pairs of electrons have on shared bonding orbitals? Why?

4. What is hybridization?

5. Read the entire laboratory activity. Form a hypothesis about the shapes of molecules made of 2, 3, 4, and 5 atoms with no lone pairs of electrons. Record your hypothesis on page 22.

Procedure

1. Inflate the round balloons to the same size and tie their ends closed.

2. Inflate four pear-shaped balloons to the same size and tie their ends closed.

3. For each balloon, make a loop of tape by wrapping the tape around two fingers. The adhesive side of the tape should face out.

4. Attach one tape loop to each balloon. On the pear-shaped balloons, put the tape on the end opposite where the knot is tied.

5. Push two of the round balloons together so that the tape loop on each balloon sticks to the other balloon, as shown in **Figure A**. This is a model of the hydrogen molecule, H_2. Describe the shape of the model in **Data Table 1**.

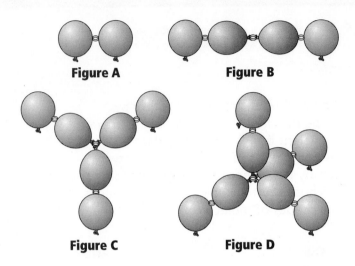

Figure A   **Figure B**

Figure C   **Figure D**

6. Disassemble the H_2 model.

7. Use string to tie together the knotted ends of two pear-shaped balloons. Attach a round balloon to the other end of each pear-shaped balloon, as shown in **Figure B.** This is a model of beryllium dichloride, $BeCl_2$. Describe the shape of the model in **Data Table 1.**

8. Use string to tie a third pear-shaped balloon to the knotted ends of the two pear-shaped balloons in the $BeCl_2$ model. Attach a round balloon to the other end of the third pear-shaped balloon. The resulting structure, which should resemble **Figure C,** is a model of aluminum trichloride, $AlCl_3$. Describe the shape of the model in **Data Table 1.**

9. Use string to tie a fourth pear-shaped balloon to the knotted ends of the three pear-shaped balloons in the $AlCl_3$ model. Attach a round balloon to the other end of the fourth pear-shaped balloon. The resulting structure, which should resemble **Figure D,** is a model of methane, CH_4. Describe the shape of the model in **Data Table 1.**

10. Remove two of the pear-shaped balloons and their attached round balloons from the CH_4 model.

11. Inflate two pear-shaped balloons so that they are at least twice the size of the other pear-shaped balloons. Tie their ends closed. Each large pear-shaped balloon represents a lone pair of electrons.

12. Use string to tie the large pear-shaped balloons to the knotted ends of the two remaining pear-shaped balloons in the partially disassembled CH_4 model. The resulting structure is a model of water, H_2O. Describe the shape of the model in **Data Table 1.**

Hypothesis

_____

_____

_____

_____

Cleanup and Disposal

1. Return all lab equipment to its proper place.

2. Wash your hands thoroughly with soap or detergent before you leave the lab.

LAB 6 **SMALL-SCALE LABORATORY MANUAL**

Data and Observations

Data Table 1		
Molecule	**Shape**	**Bond angle (°)**
H_2		
$BeCl_2$		
$AlCl_3$		
CH_4		
H_2O		

Calculate the bond angles in each of the models you constructed. Record the bond angles in **Data Table 1.**

Analyze and Conclude

1. **Formulating Models** What type of orbital is represented by a round balloon? A pear-shaped balloon? (Hint: Think about the shape of each balloon.)

   _____

   _____

2. **Applying Concepts** What hybrid orbitals are formed in each of the molecules you modeled?

   _____

   _____

   _____

3. **Observing and Inferring** Both $BeCl_2$ and H_2O contain three atoms. Do your models show that these molecules have the same shape? Explain why or why not.

   _____

   _____

   _____

   _____

4. **Predicting** Predict the shapes of the following molecules: CH_3Cl, Cl_2, CCl_4, HCl, BF_3.

   _____

   _____

   _____

LAB ⑥   SMALL-SCALE LABORATORY MANUAL

5. **Error Analysis** Compare the results of this experiment with the predictions of your hypothesis. Explain possible reasons for any disagreement.

_____

_____

_____

_____

Real-World Chemistry

1. Ethene, $H_2C = CH_2$, serves as the starting material for the synthesis of polyethylene, from which plastic bags and milk jugs are made. Ethyne, $H—C \equiv C—H$, is used as a fuel for welding torches. The double bond in ethene and the triple bond in ethyne have the same effect on molecular shape as single bonds. Predict the shapes and bond angles of ethene and ethyne.

2. Hemoglobin is an iron-containing molecule that transports oxygen in your blood. Each iron atom in hemoglobin forms bonds with five nitrogen atoms and one oxygen atom. Use the VSEPR model to predict the shape of the part of hemoglobin that consists of iron and the atoms it bonds with. (Hint: Count the number of shared electron pairs involved and refer to Table 9-3 in your textbook.)

3. Living things are made of a huge variety of different carbon-containing molecules. Many of these molecules are very large and have complex, three-dimensional shapes. Would the same variety of shapes be possible for molecules that contain beryllium instead of carbon? Explain why or why not. (Hint: Remember that carbon atoms can form bonds with other carbon atoms.)

LAB **7** **SMALL-SCALE LABORATORY MANUAL**

Solutions and Precipitates

Use with Section 10.3

Aqueous solutions of ionic compounds contain dissolved positive and negative ions. When two such solutions are mixed, the ions may take part in a double-replacement reaction. One outcome of a double-replacement reaction is the formation of a precipitate. By writing ionic equations and knowing the solubilities of specific ionic compounds, you can predict whether a precipitate will be formed.

Problem

Can you predict whether two aqueous solutions will form a precipitate when they are mixed?

Objectives

- **Write** ionic equations for mixtures of aqueous solutions.
- **Predict** which mixtures will form precipitates.
- **Observe** mixtures for precipitate formation.

Materials

1.0M $BaCl_2$
1.0M $CuSO_4$
1.0M $FeCl_3$
1.0M KI
1.0M NaCl
1.0M Na_2CO_3

1.0M NaOH
1.0M Na_2SO_4
1.0M $Pb(NO_3)_2$
24-well microplate
pipettes (9)

Safety Precautions

- Always wear safety goggles, gloves, and a lab apron.
- Use extra care when handling the solutions.
- Notify your teacher of any spills.
- Do not dispose of wastes in the sink or trash can.
- Never place the pipette in your mouth.

Pre-Lab

1. What is a double-replacement reaction?
2. What are the three types of products that can form from double-replacement reactions?
3. What is a spectator ion?
4. What is the difference between a complete ionic equation and a net ionic equation?
5. Read the entire laboratory activity. Study **Table 1.** Form a hypothesis about which mixtures listed in **Data Table 1** will form a precipitate. Explain why a precipitate will form in those mixtures. Record your hypothesis on page 26.

Table 1

Solubility of Ionic Compounds in Water						
	Anion					
Cation	Cl⁻	CO₃²⁻	I⁻	NO₃⁻	OH⁻	SO₄²⁻
Ba^{2+}	S	I	I	S	P	I
Cu^{2+}	S	I	S	S	I	S
Fe^{3+}	S	—	S	S	I	S
K^+	S	S	S	S	S	S
Na^+	S	S	S	S	S	S
Pb^{2+}	P	I	P	S	I	I
Key						
I—insoluble						
P—partially soluble						
S—soluble						

LAB 7

Procedure

1. Choose any one of the mixtures listed in **Data Table 1.** Use a pipette to add 5 mL of the first solution in that mixture to a well on the microplate.

2. Use a different pipette to add 5 mL of the second solution in the mixture to the same well. Do not allow the tip of the pipette to touch the mixture.

3. Record the number and letter of the well in **Data Table 1.**

4. Repeat steps 1–3 for the other ten mixtures listed in **Data Table 1.** Use a different well for each mixture.

Hypothesis

_____

_____

Cleanup and Disposal

1. Dispose of all chemicals and solutions as directed by your teacher.

2. Return all lab equipment to its proper place.

3. Wash your hands thoroughly before you leave the lab.

Data and Observations

Data Table 1			
Mixture	**Solutions**	**Well**	**Observations**
1	$CuSO_4$ and NaOH		
2	$FeCl_3$ and NaOH		
3	KI and NaOH		
4	KI and NaCl		
5	KI and $Pb(NO_3)_2$		
6	Na_2SO_4 and $Pb(NO_3)_2$		
7	Na_2SO_4 and $BaCl_2$		
8	Na_2CO_3 and $BaCl_2$		
9	Na_2CO_3 and KI		
10	Na_2CO_3 and $CuSO_4$		
11	NaCl and $CuSO_4$		

LAB 7

1. Carefully observe each well that contains a mixture of solutions and note whether or not a precipitate is visible. Record the results in **Data Table 1.**

2. If there are any other signs that a reaction has occurred in any of the wells, describe those signs in **Data Table 1.**

Analyze and Conclude

1. Observing and Inferring Write the numbers of the mixtures that resulted in a double-replacement reaction. Explain how you know a reaction occurred in those mixtures.

_____

_____

_____

_____

2. Applying Concepts Write the complete ionic equations of the reactions that occurred.

_____

_____

_____

_____

_____

_____

3. Thinking Critically Why is it impossible to write a net ionic equation for any of the mixtures that did not form a precipitate?

_____

_____

_____

_____

4. Error Analysis Compare the results of this lab with the predictions of your hypothesis. Explain possible reasons for any disagreement.

_____

_____

_____

_____

LAB 7

SMALL-SCALE LABORATORY MANUAL

Real-World Chemistry

1. Seawater is a dilute solution of several ionic compounds, the major one of which is sodium chloride (NaCl). One way to measure the amount of NaCl in a sample of seawater is to mix the sample with a solution of silver nitrate ($AgNO_3$). Explain how this method is likely to work. (Hint: AgCl is insoluble in water.)

2. Cells that line your stomach secrete hydrochloric acid (HCl), which helps you digest your food. When these cells secrete too much HCl, an upset stomach may result. To relieve an upset stomach, you may take an antacid, such as magnesium hydroxide, $Mg(OH)_2$. Magnesium hydroxide reacts with HCl in a double-replacement reaction, but no precipitate is formed. Write the complete and net ionic equations for this reaction. What is the product?

3. Sodium hydrogen carbonate ($NaHCO_3$) can also be used as an antacid. Write the net ionic equation for the reaction between $NaHCO_3$ and HCl. What would be one disadvantage of using $NaHCO_3$ instead of $Mg(OH)_2$ to treat an upset stomach?

LAB **8** **SMALL-SCALE LABORATORY MANUAL**

Determining Avogadro's Number

Use with Section 11.1

Avogadro hypothesized that equal numbers of moles of different gases at the same temperature and pressure contain the same number of molecules. But he never calculated what that number might be. Later on, other scientists calculated a value for Avogadro's number. In one experiment, a thin film of a chemical was spread on the surface of water. The layer was assumed to be one molecule thick, or a monolayer. In 1924, it was estimated that the number of molecules in a mole was 6.004×10^{23}.

You will cover the surface of a water sample with a monolayer of stearic acid by adding drops of stearic acid solution to the water surface. The solvent will quickly evaporate, leaving the nonpolar stearic acid molecules on the water's surface.

The mass of the stearic acid can be determined, and the number of moles of stearic acid can be calculated using the molar mass of stearic acid. The monolayer formed is one molecule thick, so if an assumption is made about the shape of a single molecule, the number of molecules in the monolayer can be estimated. Avogadro's number is then estimated as the ratio of the number of molecules of stearic acid to the number of moles of stearic acid. The closer the assumed shape is to the actual shape of the molecule, the more precise the calculation of Avogadro's number will be. In this experiment, the shape of the molecule is first assumed to be a rectangular solid and then a cylindrical solid.

Problem

How many molecules of stearic acid are in a mole of stearic acid?

Objectives

- **Measure** the diameter of stearic acid solution in a monolayer.
- **Calculate** a value for Avogadro's number.
- **Infer** which volume estimate better approximates the volume of a stearic acid molecule.

Materials

stearic acid solution
distilled water
lycopodium powder
  or talcum powder
50-mL beaker
10-mL graduated
  cylinder
metric ruler

iron ring
Pasteur pipette
  with suction bulb
large watch glass
ring stand
small test tubes (2)
test-tube rack
scoop

Safety Precautions

- **Always wear safety goggles, gloves, and a lab apron.**
- **Avoid breathing directly over the watch glass.**

Pre-Lab

1. What is the accepted value for Avogadro's number?

2. Calculate the volume of a cylinder that has a diameter of 3.00×10^{-4} cm and a height of 1.00×10^{-2} cm. ($V_{cyl} = \pi(d/2)^2 \times h$)

3. Stearic acid is a solid at room temperature and pressure. For this experiment, it must be dissolved in an appropriate solvent. Why must the chosen solvent evaporate quickly from the water's surface?

4. Read the entire laboratory activity. Two assumptions are made about the shape of a single stearic acid molecule. Form a hypothesis as to which shape you think will give the more precise value for Avogadro's number—rectangular solid or cylindrical solid. Record your hypothesis in the next column.

Procedure

1. Fill a 50-mL beaker with distilled water. Attach a suction bulb to a Pasteur pipette and fill it with distilled water. Count the number of drops needed to fill a 10-mL graduated cylinder to the 1.00 mL mark. Record the number of drops in **Data Table 1.** Repeat this process two more times.

2. Set the watch glass on a metal ring, which is attached to a ring stand. Place the ring at a level so that the top of the watch glass can be viewed at eye level.

3. Using a ruler, measure and record the diameter of the watch glass. Thoroughly wash the watch glass and rinse it several times with distilled water. **CAUTION: All soap must be rinsed off or a monolayer of molecules will not form.** Replace the watch glass on the metal ring and fill it with distilled water.

4. Pour 2 mL of stearic acid solution into a small test tube. Set the test tube in a test-tube rack. Label a second small test tube "WASTE" (material can be recycled) and set it in the test-tube rack.

5. Fill the end of a scoop with lycopodium powder and, while holding the scoop about 30 cm above the watch glass, uniformly sprinkle the powder over the surface of the water. The powder layer should be thin—like a layer of dust.

6. Rinse the Pasteur pipette with a small amount of the stearic acid solution. Put the rinsing into the test tube labeled WASTE (material can be recycled). Partially fill the Pasteur pipette with half of the remaining solution.

7. While holding the pipette directly above the center of the watch glass, squeeze out one drop of the solution.

8. Observe the drop as it spreads over the surface of the water in the watch glass. When the drop has finished spreading, add a second drop. The amount of spreading will decrease with each additional drop. Continue to add drops one at a time until the added drop does not spread. Record the total number of drops in **Data Table 2.**

9. Empty and clean the watch glass, making sure that all of the soap is removed.

10. Repeat steps 3 and 5. Fill the Pasteur pipette with the second half of the stearic acid solution. Repeat steps 7 and 8.

Hypothesis

_____

_____

_____

Cleanup and Disposal

1. Wash, dry, and store all equipment

2. Dispose of the stearic acid solution in the waste test tube in the designated container.

3. Wash your hands thoroughly with soap or detergent before you leave the lab.

Copyright © Glencoe/McGraw-Hill, a division of the McGraw-Hill Companies, Inc.

SMALL-SCALE LABORATORY MANUAL

Data and Observations

Data Table 1				
Calibration of pipette				
	Trial 1	**Trial 2**	**Trail 3**	**Average**
Number of drops in 1.00 mL				

Data Table 2		
	Trial 1	**Trial 2**
Drops of stearic acid solution needed to form monolayer		

Density of stearic acid : 0.9405 g/cm^3

Concentration of stearic acid solution: 0.10 g/L

Molar mass of stearic acid: 284.5 g/mol

Diameter of the watch glass (cm): _____

1. Calculate the average number of drops in one milliliter for your Pasteur pipette.

_____

2. Use the following equation to calculate the mass of stearic acid.
Mass of stearic acid = Concentration (g/L) $\times$ 1 L/1000 mL $\times$ 1 mL/avg. no. of drops $\times$ no. of drops to form monolayer

_____

3. Calculate the volume of the monolayer by dividing the mass of stearic acid (step 2) by the density of stearic acid.

_____

4. The watch glass is circular, so the monolayer of stearic acid covering its surface is a cylinder. To calculate the thickness of the monolayer, divide the volume of the monolayer (step 3) by the area of the circle. [$Area = \pi(diameter(cm)/2)^2$]

_____

5. The monolayer is one molecule thick, so the thickness of a stearic acid molecule is equal to the length of the molecule. If the length of the molecule is assumed to be six times the width and depth, calculate the volume of one molecule when the shape of the stearic acid molecule is assumed to be a rectangular solid. ($V_{rec} = l \times w \times d$); ($l = 6w = 6d$)

_____

6. Find the number of molecules by dividing the volume of the monolayer (step 3) by the volume of one molecule (step 5).

_____

7. Calculate the number of moles of stearic acid in the monolayer by dividing the mass of stearic acid (step 2) by the molar mass of stearic acid.

_____

8. To calculate Avogadro's number when the stearic acid molecule is a rectangular solid, divide the number of molecules (step 6) by the number of moles (step 7).

_____

9. If the length of the molecule is assumed to be six times the diameter, calculate the volume of one molecule when the shape of the stearic acid molecule is assumed to be a cylindrical solid. $(V_{cyl} = l \times (\pi(d/2)^2)$; $(l = 6d)$

_____

10. To find the number of molecules, divide the volume of the monolayer (step 3) by the volume of one molecule (step 9).

_____

11. Recalculate Avogadro's number, assuming the stearic acid molecule is a cylindrical solid. Divide the number of molecules (step 10) by the number of moles (step 7).

_____

Analyze and Conclude

1. **Error Analysis** The accepted value for Avogadro's number is 6.022×10^{23} particles per mole. Calculate the percent error for each of your calculations of Avogadro's number.

_____

2. **Drawing a Conclusion** Which of your two calculations came closer to the accepted value for Avogadro's number—the calculation made assuming a rectangular solid or the calculation made assuming a cylindrical solid?

_____

3. **Observing and Inferring** Which assumption is closer to the actual shape of the stearic acid molecule—rectangular solid or cylindrical solid?

_____

Real-World Chemistry

To calculate Avogadro's number, chemists made assumptions about the shape of a single molecule. Chemists who use computer simulations to model compounds and chemical reactions also make simplifying assumptions about molecular shape in order to perform calculations needed for their research. Identify and investigate a program used by chemists for computer simulation and list some of the limitations and assumptions this program makes.

LAB **9** **SMALL-SCALE LABORATORY MANUAL**

Measuring Boiling Point

Use with Section 13.4

Vaporization is the phase change in which a liquid changes to a gas. When vaporization occurs throughout a liquid instead of only at the surface, the liquid is said to be boiling. The temperature at which boiling occurs, called the boiling point, varies for different substances. Two factors—molar mass and the ability to form hydrogen bonds—are most important in determining boiling point. In general, boiling points are higher for more massive molecules and for molecules that form hydrogen bonds.

Problem

How can you compare the boiling points of substances?

Objectives

- **Measure** the boiling points of three known liquids.
- **Correlate** boiling point with molar mass and the ability to form hydrogen bonds.
- **Identify** an unknown liquid by its boiling point.

Materials

acetone
ethanol
1-propanol
100-mL beaker
thermometer
 (−10°C to 100°C)
capillary tubes,
 sealed at one
 end (3)

small test tubes (3)
thin-stem pipette
hot plate
ring stand
thermometer clamp
rubber band
glass stirring rod

Safety Precautions

- **Always wear safety goggles, gloves, and a lab apron.**
- **Notify your teacher of any spills.**
- **Use caution and proper protection when handling hot objects.**
- **Do not dispose of wastes in the sink or trash can.**
- **Never place the pipette in your mouth.**
- **Acetone, ethanol, and propanol are all flammable chemicals.**

Pre-Lab

1. Contrast evaporation and boiling.

2. Define *vapor pressure*.

3. What is the relationship between vapor pressure and external pressure when a liquid is at its boiling point?

4. What are the signs that a liquid has reached its boiling point?

5. Read the entire laboratory activity. Form a hypothesis about which of the substances you will test has the highest boiling point and which has the lowest boiling point. Explain your reasoning. Record your hypothesis on page 34.

Procedure

1. Set the hot plate on the base of the ring stand.

2. Fill the beaker about two-thirds full with tap water. Place the beaker on the hot plate.

3. Use the thermometer clamp to attach the thermometer to the ring stand. Lower the clamp so the thermometer is in the water, as shown in **Figure A** on page 34.

4. Turn the hot plate on to a medium setting. While the water is heating, complete steps 5 and 6.

5. Place a clean capillary tube with the sealed end up into a clean, small test tube.

6. Use the pipette to add 3 mL of one of the known liquids to the test tube.

7. When the water temperature has reached approximately 80°C, raise the clamp so the thermometer is above the beaker. **CAUTION: The thermometer will be hot.**

8. Use the rubber band to attach the test tube to the thermometer. The bottom of the test tube should be at the same level as the bulb of the thermometer.

9. Lower the clamp so the test tube–thermometer assembly is in the water. The top of the assembly should be above the surface of the water, as shown in **Figure B.**

10. Look for bubbles coming from the open end of the capillary tube. If you do not see any bubbles, continue heating the water until you do.

11. When a steady stream of bubbles issues from the open end of the capillary tube, turn off the hot plate.

12. Use the glass stirring rod to stir the water constantly until the stream of bubbles stops. Immediately read the temperature of the water to the nearest 0.1°C. This is the boiling point of the liquid in the capillary tube. Record the temperature in **Data Table 1.**

Figure B

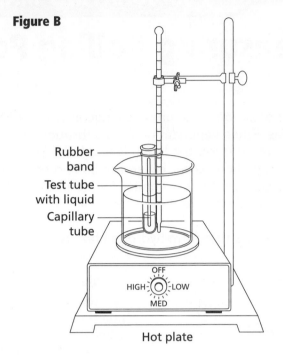

Rubber band
Test tube with liquid
Capillary tube

OFF
HIGH—LOW
MED

Hot plate

13. Repeat steps 4–12 with the other two known liquids and the unknown liquid. Use distilled water to clean the pipettes before drawing up a different liquid.

Hypothesis

_____

_____

_____

_____

Cleanup and Disposal

1. Dispose of all materials as directed by your teacher.

2. Return all lab equipment to its proper place.

3. Wash your hands thoroughly with soap or detergent before you leave the lab.

Figure A

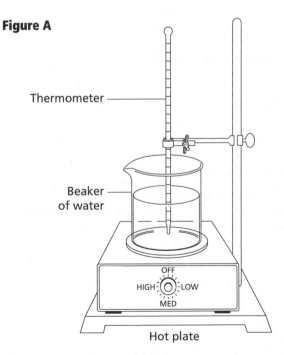

Thermometer

Beaker of water

OFF
HIGH—LOW
MED

Hot plate

LAB (9)

SMALL-SCALE LABORATORY MANUAL

Data and Observations

Data Table 1				
Liquid	Molar formula	Molar mass (g)	Hydrogen bonding?	Boiling point (°C)
Acetone	C_3H_6O		no	
Ethanol	C_2H_5O		yes	
1-propanol	C_3H_8O		yes	
Unknown	—	—	—	

Analyze and Conclude

1. **Measuring and Using Numbers** Calculate the molar mass of each known liquid. Record the results in **Data Table 1.**

2. **Thinking Critically** Why did you record the temperature when the bubbles stopped appearing as the boiling point of each liquid?

   _____

   _____

   _____

3. **Observing and Inferring** Identify the unknown liquid by comparing its boiling point with the boiling points of the known liquids.

   _____

4. **Drawing a Conclusion** Based on your results, which factor—molar mass or hydrogen bonding—seems to be more important in determining boiling point? Explain your reasoning.

   _____

   _____

   _____

   _____

5. **Acquiring and Analyzing Information** Look up the accepted boiling point of each known liquid.

   _____

   _____

6. **Error Analysis** Compare the boiling point you measured for each known liquid with the accepted boiling point. Calculate the percent error, if any. Explain possible sources of error in the lab.

_____

_____

_____

_____

_____

Real-World Chemistry

1. The amount of time it takes to cook noodles depends on the temperature of the water that they are cooked in. Would it take longer to cook noodles in boiling water at sea level or at an altitude of 3000 m? Explain.

2. Why are foods such as french fries and fried chicken cooked in oil rather than in water? (Hint: Cooking oil is a mixture of fat molecules whose molar masses may be 800 g or more.)

3. Most automobile engines are cooled by a mixture of water and antifreeze, which consists mostly of 1,2-ethanediol (commonly called ethylene glycol). Why is such a mixture better at cooling an engine than water alone? (Hint: The boiling point of 1,2-ethanediol is 197°C.)

LAB **10** SMALL-SCALE LABORATORY MANUAL

Relating Gas Pressure and Gas Volume

The gas laws describe the interdependence of three variables—pressure, volume, and temperature—that determine the behavior of gases. One of the gas laws, Boyle's law, states how gas pressure and gas volume are related. Boyle's law applies to ideal gases, which obey all of the assumptions made by the kinetic theory. With a simple laboratory setup, you can test how well Boyle's law applies to real gases.

Problem

How does changing the pressure of a gas affect the volume of the gas?

Objectives

- **Measure** the volume of the air sample at different pressures.
- **Make and use a graph** of volume versus pressure to illustrate the mathematical relationship.

Materials

flat objects that can be stacked (4)
Boyle's law apparatus
carpet thread
balance
metric ruler

Safety Precautions

- **Always wear safety goggles, gloves, and a lab apron.**
- **Gas under pressure can be hazardous. Use the Boyle's law apparatus only as directed.**

Pre-Lab

1. State Boyle's law.
2. Define pressure.
3. A force of 12.7 N is applied to a circular disk whose radius is 6.20 cm. Calculate the pressure (in N/m^2) applied to the disk. (Hint: The area of a circle = $\pi \times radius^2$.)
4. Suppose there is an inverse relationship between two variables, x and y. What happens to y as x increases?
5. Read the entire laboratory activity. Form a hypothesis about how the volume of the air sample will change as the pressure on the sample increases. Record your hypothesis on page 38.

Procedure

1. Use the balance to measure the mass of each object to the nearest gram. Record the masses in **Data Table 1.**
2. Pull the plunger all the way out of the Boyle's law apparatus. Use the ruler to measure the diameter of the head of the plunger to the nearest millimeter. Record the diameter in **Data Table 1.**
3. Insert a length of carpet thread into the barrel of the Boyle's law apparatus. Leave one end of the thread hanging out of the apparatus, as shown in **Figure A.**

SMALL-SCALE LABORATORY MANUAL

Figure A

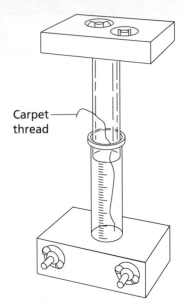

Carpet thread

4. Push the plunger back into the barrel until the head of the plunger is near the 35 cm³ mark on the barrel. The thread will make a small space for air to escape past the head as you do this.

5. While holding the plunger in place, carefully remove the thread. Twist the plunger several times to reduce friction between the head and the barrel.

6. Measure the volume to the nearest 0.1 cm³. Record the volume in **Data Table 1** as the volume for zero total mass under *Trial 1*.

7. Carefully place the first mass on top of the plunger.

8. While stabilizing the apparatus, twist the plunger several times to reduce friction. Measure and record the volume to the nearest 0.1 cm³ under *Trial 1*.

9. Carefully stack the second mass on top of the first mass. Repeat step 8.

10. Carefully stack the third mass on top of the other two masses. Repeat step 8.

11. Carefully stack the fourth mass on top of the other three masses. Repeat step 8.

12. Remove all four masses. Repeat steps 6–11 two more times. Record the results in **Data Table 1** under *Trial 2* and *Trial 3*.

Hypothesis

_____

_____

Cleanup and Disposal

1. Make sure your balance is left in the same condition as you found it.

2. Return all lab equipment to its proper place.

Data and Observations

Data Table 1								
Mass of object 1 (g):				Mass of object 3 (g):				
Mass of object 2 (g):				Mass of object 4 (g):				
Diameter of plunger head (mm):				Area of plunger head (m²):				
Stacked objects	**Total mass (kg)**	**Force (N)**	**Pressure (N/m²)**	**Total pressure (N/m²)**	**Volume (cm³)**			
					Trial 1	**Trial 2**	**Trial 3**	**Average**
none	0							
1								
1, 2								
1, 2, 3								
1, 2, 3, 4								

1. Calculate the cross-sectional area (in m^2) of the head of the plunger. (Remember that radius = diameter/2.) Record the result in **Data Table 1**.

2. Calculate the total mass (in kg) when one, two, three, or all four objects were placed on the apparatus. Record the results in **Data Table 1**.

3. Calculate the force (in N) exerted on the plunger by each total mass. Use the following formula: force (N) = mass (kg) $\times$ 9.80 m/s^2. Record the results in **Data Table 1**.

4. Calculate the pressure (in N/m^2) exerted on the plunger by each total mass. (Hint: Recall the definition of pressure.) Record the results in **Data Table 1**.

5. The atmosphere also exerts pressure on the plunger. For each total mass, calculate the total pressure by adding atmospheric pressure to the pressure exerted by stacked objects. (Unless your teacher instructs you otherwise, assume that atmospheric pressure = 1.0 $\times$ 10^5 N/m^2.) Record the results in **Data Table 1**.

6. For each total mass, calculate the average volume by adding the volumes in each trial and dividing by 3. Record the results in **Data Table 1**.

Analyze and Conclude

1. **Making and Using Graphs** Make a graph of volume versus pressure. Plot the average volume on the vertical axis and the total pressure on the horizontal axis. Draw lines between the data points, label both axes, and give the graph a title.

2. **Collecting and Interpreting Data** Describe the relationship between average volume and total pressure as shown by the results in **Data Table 1** and on your graph.

_____

_____

_____

_____

3. **Applying Concepts** Would your results have been different if the temperature of the apparatus had changed during the experiment? Explain.

_____

_____

_____

_____

4. Error Analysis Compare the results of this experiment with your hypothesis. Explain possible reasons for any disagreement.

_____

_____

_____

Real-World Chemistry

1. Most gasoline engines have a set of pistons that move up and down inside hollow cylinders. Each up-and-down movement is called a stroke. In the compression stroke, the pistons reduce the volume (compress) a gaseous mixture of fuel and air in the cylinders. A typical gasoline engine in a modern automobile may have a compression ratio of 8 to 1. This means that the volume of gas in each cylinder at the start of the compression stroke is 8 times the volume at the end of the stroke. If the gas is at atmospheric pressure (1.0×10^5 N/m^2) at the start of a compression stroke, what is the pressure of the gas at the end of the stroke? Assume the temperature of the gas does not change during the stroke.

2. The helium in a weather balloon occupies a volume of 200.0 L when the balloon is released at sea level, where the atmospheric pressure is 1.0×10^5 N/m^2. What is the volume of the helium when the balloon is at an altitude of 10 700 m, where the surrounding air pressure is 2.3×10^4 N/m^2? Assume the temperature is the same at the two locations.

3. As a scuba diver descends through the water, the surrounding water pressure increases. The gases in the diver's body, including any small bubbles that may be in the blood vessels, are at the same pressure as the surrounding water. What happens to these bubbles as the diver ascends? Why is it dangerous for a diver to ascend too quickly?

LAB 11 SMALL-SCALE LABORATORY MANUAL

Effect of Temperature on Solubility

Use with Section 15.1

For a solute to dissolve in a solvent, the solute and solvent particles must collide with each other. Any factor that affects the frequency of these collisions is likely to affect the rate at which the solute dissolves. One important factor is temperature. As temperature increases, the average kinetic energy of solute and solvent particles increases. Collisions occur more frequently and with greater energy. Therefore, many solutes dissolve more rapidly at higher temperatures. For other solutes, however, the opposite is true. In this activity, you will determine the effects of temperature on the solution process.

Problem

How can you determine the effect of temperature on the rate at which ammonia gas dissolves in water?

Objectives

- **Collect** ammonia gas from a concentrated ammonia solution.
- **Measure** the time required for ammonia gas to dissolve in water at four different temperatures.
- **Relate** the time it takes the ammonia to dissolve to solubility.

Materials

concentrated ammonia solution
400-mL beaker
250-mL beaker
100-mL beaker
thin-stem pipette

wide-stem pipette
scissors
metric ruler
stopwatch
crushed ice
fume hood

Safety Precautions

- Always wear safety goggles, gloves, and a lab apron.
- Ammonia will irritate the eyes, skin, and respiratory tract. Use extra care when handling the concentrated ammonia solution.
- Notify your teacher of any spills.
- Use caution and proper protection when handling hot objects.
- Do not dispose of wastes in the sink or trash can.

Pre-Lab

1. What is solubility?

2. Refer to Table 15-2 in your textbook. How does decreasing the temperature affect the solubility of most solids that are dissolved in water?

3. How does decreasing the temperature affect the solubility of gases in liquid solvents?

4. How would the solubility of a gas in a liquid change if the pressure of the gas above the liquid was doubled? Explain why.

5. Read the entire laboratory activity. Form a hypothesis about how decreasing the temperature will affect the time required for ammonia to dissolve in water. Explain why decreasing the temperature should have this effect. Record your hypothesis on page 42.

LAB ⑪   **SMALL-SCALE LABORATORY MANUAL**

Procedure

1. Use scissors to cut the tip off the wide-stem pipette, leaving the stem about 4 cm long. This is the collecting pipette.

2. Place the three beakers used in this activity under the fume hood. Beakers must remain beneath the fume hood throughout the entire procedure. Fill the 400-mL beaker with about 350 mL of hot tap water.

3. Working under the fume hood, halfway fill the thin-stem pipette with concentrated ammonia solution. This is the generating pipette. Keep the pipette in the fume hood at all times.

4. Turn the generating pipette bulb-end down and submerge the bulb in the beaker of hot water. Cover the tip of the generating pipette with the collecting pipette, as shown in **Figure A.**

5. As the ammonia solution warms in the generating pipette, ammonia gas leaves the solution and begins filling the bulb of the collecting pipette. Squeeze the collecting pipette several times to expel all of the air and help the ammonia gas completely fill the collecting pipette.

Figure A

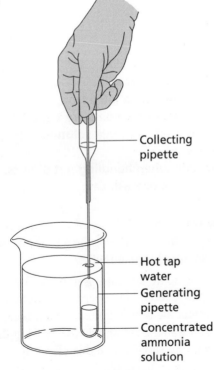

— Collecting pipette

— Hot tap water

— Generating pipette

— Concentrated ammonia solution

Figure B

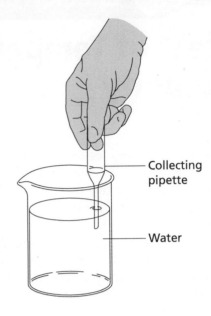

— Collecting pipette

— Water

6. Fill the 250-mL beaker with 200 mL of hot tap water. Measure the temperature of the water to the nearest 0.1°C. Record the temperature in **Data Table 1.**

7. After collecting ammonia gas for 3–4 min, remove the collecting pipette from the generating pipette. Set the generating pipette bulb down in the 100-mL beaker.

8. Submerge the tip of the collecting pipette in the hot water in the 250-mL beaker, as shown in **Figure B.** Start the stopwatch. Keep the level of water in the pipette near the level in the beaker by lowering the pipette as it fills with water.

9. Stop the stopwatch when the gas in the collecting pipette has dissolved completely. The gas is completely dissolved when the pipette is full of water. Record the time in **Data Table 1.**

10. Repeat steps 2 through 9, filling the 250-mL beaker with 200 mL of each of the following.
    a. a 50-50 mixture of hot tap water and cold tap water
    b. cold tap water
    c. a mixture of cold tap water and ice

LAB (11)   SMALL-SCALE LABORATORY MANUAL

Hypothesis

_____

_____

_____

Cleanup and Disposal

1. Dispose of all solutions as directed by your teacher.
2. Return all lab equipment to its proper place.
3. Wash your hands thoroughly with soap or detergent before leaving the lab.

Data and Observations

Data Table 1			
	Temperature (°C)	**Temperature (K)**	**Time (s)**
Hot water			
Hot water + cold water			
Cold water			
Cold water + ice			

Convert each temperature in degrees Celsius to kelvin by adding 273. Record the results in **Data Table 1.**

Analyze and Conclude

1. **Thinking Critically** How can you be sure that the collecting pipette was filled with ammonia (NH_3) instead of air in step 5? (Hint: Air is composed mostly of N_2 and O_2. Consider the density of the gases involved.)

_____

_____

_____

_____

_____

2. **Applying Concepts** Explain why water was drawn into the collecting pipette in step 8.

_____

_____

_____

_____

3. **Making and Using Graphs** Make a graph of dissolving time (in seconds) versus temperature (in kelvins). Connect the data points, label the axes, and title the graph.

4. **Observing and Inferring** Based on your results, what can you infer about the effect of temperature on the solubility of ammonia in water? Compare this conclusion with the data given for ammonia in Table 15-2 in your textbook.

_____

_____

_____

_____

_____

_____

5. **Error Analysis** How do your results compare with the predictions of your hypothesis? Provide an explanation for any disagreement.

_____

_____

_____

_____

_____

_____

Real-World Chemistry

1. Much of the carbon dioxide produced by living things and by the burning of fossil fuels is dissolved in ocean water. Explain how the level of carbon dioxide in the atmosphere would be affected if ocean temperatures were to increase.

2. Some fish that live in stagnant pools come to the surface occasionally to gulp air. Such fish will gulp air more frequently if the water in the pools is warm. Explain why.

3. Is a bottle of carbonated beverage at room temperature more likely to bubble over when opened than one that has been refrigerated overnight? Explain.

LAB 12 SMALL-SCALE LABORATORY MANUAL

Specific Heat of Metals

Use with Section 16.2

Heat flows from a warmer object to a cooler object. As heat flows, the temperature of the warmer object decreases and the temperature of the cooler object increases. The magnitude of the temperature change depends in part upon what each object is made of. Objects that experience a large temperature change when they absorb or release a given amount of heat have a low specific heat. Objects that experience a small temperature change for a given amount of heat transfer have a high specific heat.

Problem

How can you use water to measure the specific heat of metals?

Objectives

• **Construct** a calorimeter.
• **Measure** changes in the temperature of water in the calorimeter when warmer metals are added.
• **Calculate** the specific heat of each metal.

Materials

aluminum, iron, and lead samples
plastic-foam cups (2)
400-mL beakers (2)
100-mL graduated cylinder

large test tubes (3)
boiling chips
scissors
balance
hot plate
thermometer
test-tube rack

Safety Precautions

• Always wear safety goggles, gloves, and a lab apron.
• Broken glassware may have sharp edges. Be careful when using scissors.
• Use caution and proper protection when handling hot objects.
• Avoid spilling water on the hot plate power cord.
• Wipe up any water spills immediately to avoid slipping.

Pre-Lab

1. Define *specific heat*.

2. A sample of substance X has a mass of 123 g. When the sample releases 795 J of heat, its temperature falls from 45.1°C to 17.6°C. What is the specific heat of substance X?

3. What is a calorimeter?

4. Why is it important that a calorimeter be made of an insulating material?

5. Read the entire laboratory activity. Form a hypothesis about which of the three metals will cause the largest change in water temperature for its mass. Explain your reasoning. Record your hypothesis on page 46.

Procedure

1. Use scissors to remove the lip from one of the plastic-foam cups. As shown in **Figure A,** this cup will be the top of the calorimeter. Invert it and set it on top of the other cup, which will be the bottom of the calorimeter.

2. Use a pencil to punch a hole in the center of the top of the calorimeter. The hole should be large enough to hold the thermometer.

3. Place the calorimeter in one of the beakers to keep it from tipping over.

4. Measure the mass of each metal sample to the nearest 0.1 g. Record the masses in **Data Table 1.** Place each metal in a separate test tube, and label each tube.

LAB 12

Figure A

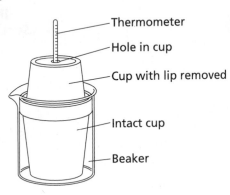

- Thermometer
- Hole in cup
- Cup with lip removed
- Intact cup
- Beaker

5. Add about 300 mL of water and a few boiling chips to the second beaker. Place all three test tubes in the beaker, as shown in **Figure B.**

6. Be sure the water level in the beaker is above the tops of the metal samples. Add more water to the beaker if necessary, but do not allow any water to get into the test tubes.

7. Set the beaker of water and test tubes on the hot plate. Turn the hot plate on and heat the water to a boil.

8. While the water is heating, pour about 75 mL of cold water into the graduated cylinder. Measure the volume to the nearest 0.1 mL. Record the volume in the data table column for aluminum.

9. Pour the cold water into the calorimeter. With the top of the calorimeter off, measure the temperature of the water every minute until it stays the same for 3 min. Record this temperature as the initial water temperature in the data table column for aluminum.

10. After the water has been boiling for 10 min, measure the temperature of the boiling water. You can assume that the metal samples are at the same temperature as the water. Record the temperature as the initial metal temperature in the data table columns for each metal. Keep the water boiling.

11. Use the test-tube holder to remove the test tube that contains the aluminum sample. **CAUTION: Carefully slide the aluminum into the water in the calorimeter without splashing.** Quickly put the top on the calorimeter.

12. Insert the thermometer through the hole in the calorimeter top until the tip of the thermometer touches the bottom of the calorimeter.

13. Gently swirl the beaker containing the calorimeter for 30 s while you monitor the temperature. Do not allow the metal sample to hit the thermometer. Record the highest temperature attained by the water as the final temperature in the data table column for aluminum.

14. Remove the aluminum sample from the calorimeter. Pour the water down the drain.

15. Repeat steps 8, 9, and 11–14 for the iron and lead samples.

Hypothesis

_____

_____

_____

_____

Cleanup and Disposal

1. Turn off the hot plate. After the boiling water has cooled, pour it down the drain.

2. Dry the metal samples with a paper towel.

3. Make sure your balance is left in the same condition as you found it.

4. Return the metal samples and lab equipment to their proper places.

5. Wash your hands thoroughly with soap or detergent before you leave the lab.

Figure B

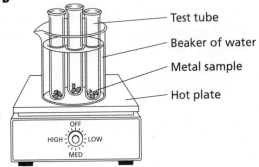

- Test tube
- Beaker of water
- Metal sample
- Hot plate

Copyright © Glencoe/McGraw-Hill, a division of the McGraw-Hill Companies, Inc.

LAB (12)   SMALL-SCALE LABORATORY MANUAL

Data and Observations

Data Table 1			
	Aluminum	**Iron**	**Lead**
Mass of metal (g)			
Volume of water (mL)			
Initial water temperature (°C)			
Initial metal temperature (°C)			
Final temperature (°C)			
Change in water temperature (°C)			
Change in metal temperature (°C)			
Heat gained by water (J)			
Specific heat, J/(g·°C)			

1. Calculate the change in water temperature caused by each metal by subtracting the initial water temperature from the final temperature. Record the results in **Data Table 1.**

2. Calculate the change in each metal's temperature by subtracting the final temperature from the initial metal temperature. Record the results in **Data Table 1.**

3. Use the equation in Section 16.1 of your textbook to calculate the amount of heat gained by the water from each metal. (To determine the mass of water, assume the density of water is 1.00 g/mL.) Record the results in **Data Table 1.**

4. Use the same equation to calculate the specific heat of each metal. (Rearrange the equation to solve for specific heat, and assume that the amount of heat lost by the metal equals the amount of heat gained by the water.) Record the results in **Data Table 1.**

Analyze and Conclude

1. **Applying Concepts** To calculate each metal's specific heat, you assumed that the amount of heat lost by the metal equals the amount of heat gained by the water. What factors determine whether this assumption is valid or not? (Hint: Identify the system and the surroundings in this experiment.)

_____

_____

_____

_____

_____

2. Drawing a Conclusion For each metal, divide the change in water temperature by the mass of the metal. Use the results of this calculation to evaluate your hypothesis.

_____

_____

_____

_____

3. Observing and Inferring Which of these metals must release the most heat to experience a given decrease in temperature per gram of metal? Explain.

_____

_____

_____

_____

4. Error Analysis Compare the specific heats you calculated for aluminum, iron, and lead with the values given in **Table 16-2** of your textbook. Calculate the percent error if any. Explain possible sources of error in the lab.

_____

_____

_____

_____

Real-World Chemistry

1. Would a fishing sinker dropped into an ice-covered lake reach the temperature of the lake water more quickly if the sinker was made of iron or lead? Use your data on the specific heats of these metals to explain your answer. (Assume the sinkers have a starting temperature of 37°C and have the same shape and mass.)

2. It is possible to remove a sheet of aluminum foil from a hot oven with your bare hands without burning yourself. However, you will surely burn yourself if you touch a thick aluminum pan in the same oven with your bare hands. Why?

3. One way to identify the composition of metal fragments found at the site of an explosion is to measure the specific heat of the fragments. Suppose a fragment is found to have a specific heat of 0.129 J/(g·°C). Would this information alone be enough to identify the metal in the fragment? Explain why or why not. If not, suggest a method for identifying the metal that would not require any additional equipment.

LAB 13 **SMALL-SCALE LABORATORY MANUAL**

Energy Changes in Chemical and Physical Processes

Use with Section 16.5

When a chemical or physical process occurs, heat (enthalpy) may be absorbed or released by the system, and the entropy, or disorder, of the system may increase or decrease. Whether a process is spontaneous or not depends upon whether the change in enthalpy of the system (ΔH_{system}) and the change in entropy of the system (ΔS_{system}) are positive or negative. A process is always spontaneous if ΔH_{system} is negative and ΔS_{system} is positive, whereas a process is never spontaneous if ΔH_{system} is positive and ΔS_{system} is negative. Processes in which ΔH_{system} and ΔS_{system} are both positive or both negative are spontaneous only at higher or lower temperatures, respectively. In this activity, you will determine whether some chemical and physical processes are spontaneous.

Problem

How can you determine whether a chemical or physical process is spontaneous?

Objectives

- **Measure** the temperature of four systems before and after a chemical or physical process.
- **Calculate** the change in temperature of each system during the process.
- **Observe** physical changes that occur during each process.
- **Deduce** whether each process is spontaneous.

Materials

$NH_4Cl(s)$
$NaHCO_3(s)$
$6M$ HCl
24-well microplate
thin-stem
  pipettes (2)

thermometer
scissors
distilled water
toothpicks (1 box)

Safety Precautions

- Always wear safety goggles, gloves, and a lab apron.
- Use extra care when handling all chemicals.
- Notify your teacher of any spills.
- Do not dispose of wastes in the sink or trash can.
- Never place a pipette in your mouth.

Pre-Lab

1. Contrast exothermic and endothermic reactions and processes.

2. Is ΔH_{system} positive or negative in an exothermic process? In an endothermic process?

3. What usually happens to the entropy of a system when a solid or liquid dissolves to form a solution?

4. Read the entire laboratory activity. Write the equation that relates free energy change (ΔG_{system}), ΔH_{system}, ΔS_{system}, and temperature.

5. Is a process spontaneous when ΔG_{system} is positive or negative?

Procedure

1. Use a thermometer to measure the temperature of the air in the room. You may assume that all of the chemicals you will use in this experiment are at room temperature. Record this temperature in **Data Table 1.**

2. Make a chemical microscoop by using scissors to cut off the end of the bulb of a pipette, as shown in **Figure A.**

Figure A

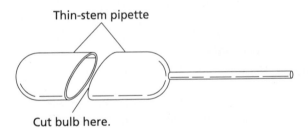

Thin-stem pipette

Cut bulb here.

3. Place a half microscoop of solid NH_4Cl in each of wells A1 and B1 on the microplate.

4. Place a half microscoop of solid $NaHCO_3$ in each of wells A2 and B2 on the microplate.

5. Use the other pipette to add a half pipette of distilled water to well A1.

6. Stir the mixture with a toothpick. Measure the temperature of the mixture. Record the temperature in **Data Table 1.** Also record any physical changes you observe.

7. Rinse the thermometer in cold water.

8. Add a half pipette of distilled water to well A2. Repeat steps 6 and 7.

9. Add a half pipette of 6*M* HCl to well B1. Repeat steps 6 and 7.

10. Add a half pipette of 6*M* HCl to well B2. Repeat steps 6 and 7.

Cleanup and Disposal

1. Dispose of all chemicals and solutions as directed by your teacher.

2. Return all lab equipment to its proper place.

3. Wash your hands thoroughly with soap or detergent before you leave the lab.

Data and Observations

Well	Contents	Temperature (°C)		Temperature change (°C)	Observations
		Before mixing	After mixing		
A1	$NH_4Cl + H_2O$				
A2	$NaHCO_3 + H_2O$				
B1	$NH_4Cl + HCl$				
B2	$NaHCO_3 + HCl$				

Data Table 1

Calculate the temperature change in each well by subtracting the temperature before mixing from the temperature after mixing. Record the results in **Data Table 1.**

LAB 13 SMALL-SCALE LABORATORY MANUAL

Analyze and Conclude

1. **Thinking Critically** Why is it valid to assume that all chemicals were at room temperature before they were mixed?

   _____

   _____

2. **Classifying** Classify the process that occurred in each well as endothermic or exothermic.

   _____

   _____

3. **Applying Concepts** Is ΔH for each process positive or negative?

   _____

   _____

4. **Observing and Inferring** Is ΔS for each process positive or negative? (Hint: Think about the physical change that occurred in each process.)

   _____

   _____

5. **Drawing a Conclusion** Under what conditions will each process occur spontaneously?

   _____

   _____

   _____

Real-World Chemistry

1. Diamonds are highly valued as gems for jewelry and are also used in industry to make abrasives and cutting tools. Both diamond ($S = +2.4$ J/K) and graphite ($S = +5.7$ J/K) are made of pure carbon. Under what conditions, if any, is the conversion of graphite to diamond spontaneous ($\Delta H_{system} = +1.90$ kJ)? Explain.

2. Benzene can be added to gasoline to make an alternative fuel. Is the combustion of benzene spontaneous at 25°C? In the combustion reaction, $\Delta H_{system} = -6535$ kJ and $\Delta S_{system} = -439.1$ J/K.

3. Ammonia (NH_3) is used as a refrigerant and as a starting material in the manufacture of fertilizer and explosives. Under the right conditions, solid NH_4Cl decomposes into NH_3 and HCl. In the decomposition reaction, $\Delta H_{system} = +176$ kJ and $\Delta S_{system} = 285$ J/K. What is the lowest temperature at which the reaction will occur spontaneously? (Hint: Assume $\Delta G_{system} = -0.1$ kJ at that temperature.)

LAB 14 SMALL-SCALE LABORATORY MANUAL

Determining Reaction Orders

Use with Section 17.3

Crystal violet is a biological stain that is used in fingerprinting and identifying bacteria. One reason crystal violet is used for these identifications is that it is blue-violet in acidic solutions and colorless in basic solutions. The color change is represented by the chemical equation between the acidic form of crystal violet (CV^+) and NaOH.

$$C_{25}H_{30}N_3Cl + NaOH \rightarrow C_{25}H_{30}N_3OH + NaCl$$
blue-violet (CV^+)   colorless (CV–OH)

Rate is the change in any measurable property per unit of time. Rate is usually expressed as the change in concentration of a reactant per unit of time. The general rate law indicates how the reaction rate is affected by changes in reactant concentrations. Because chemical reactions take place in a series of steps, the reaction rate depends on the slowest step. Therefore, the rate law describes the slowest, or rate-limiting, step in the reaction.

The general rate law for the reaction between CV^+ and NaOH has the following form in which superscripts are whole numbers that represent the relationship between the rate and the reactant concentration.

$$Rate = k[CV^+]^n[NaOH]^m$$

If the superscript is equal to zero, the concentration does not affect the reaction rate. A value of 1 means the rate doubles as the concentration doubles, and a value of 2 means the rate quadruples as the concentration doubles. Values for the superscripts must be determined experimentally.

In this activity, you will measure the time needed for the color of CV^+ to disappear as CV–OH is formed. The reaction is complete when the solution becomes colorless. The time and concentration data will be used to calculate the rate of reaction. By determining the rate experimentally with varying concentrations of reactants, the values for m and n in the general rate law can be determined.

Problem
What is the general rate equation for the reaction between crystal violet and sodium hydroxide?

Objectives
- **Measure** the time needed for reactions to occur.
- **Compare** rates of chemical reactions.
- **Infer** general rate equation from experimental data.
- **Determine** a value for the order of reaction from experimental data.

Materials
$2.0 \times 10^{-4}M$ crystal violet solution
$1.0M$ NaOH solution
24-well microplate with deep wells
droppers (3)
sheets of white paper (15)
stopwatch or clock with second hand
toothpicks (3)
distilled water

LAB 14

SMALL-SCALE LABORATORY MANUAL

Safety Precautions

- Always wear safety goggles, gloves, and a lab apron.
- Crystal violet is moderately toxic and a tissue irritant.
- NaOH is corrosive.
- When water and NaOH are mixed, much heat is released.

Pre-Lab

1. What is the likely value(s) of *m* if the [NaOH] participates in the rate-limiting step of the reaction?

2. How can you tell when the reaction is complete?

3. What is the purpose of placing the well plate on a white sheet of paper?

4. Explain why the value of the average rate is not calculated using the sodium hydroxide concentrations.

5. Read the entire lab activity. Scientists use the balanced chemical equation and previous knowledge of how chemicals react with one another to predict what the rate law might be. Then they run experiments to test their hypotheses. Form a hypothesis as to the values of *m* and *n* in the general rate law for this experiment. Record your hypothesis in the next column.

Procedure

1. Set a 24-well microplate on a sheet of white paper. In three separate wells, mix the water and NaOH in the proportions listed in **Data Table 1**. Use a separate dropper for each liquid. Label the wells by reaction number.

2. Using the third dropper, add the appropriate amount of crystal violet indicated in **Data Table 1** for reaction 1.

3. Check the time (or set the stopwatch) as you add the crystal violet.

4. Stir the mixture with a toothpick. Continue stirring until the blue color disappears and the solution is colorless.

5. As soon as the solution becomes colorless, record the number of seconds it took for the color to disappear in **Data Table 1.**

6. Repeat steps 2 to 5 for reaction mixtures 2 and 3.

Hypothesis

_____

_____

_____

_____

Cleanup and Disposal

1. Wash, dry, and store all glassware.

2. Return all lab equipment to its proper place.

3. Dispose of all solutions as directed by your teacher.

4. Wash your hands thoroughly with soap or detergent before you leave the lab.

Data and Observations

Data Table 1				
Reaction mixture	**Crystal violet (drops)**	**0.1M NaOH (drops)**	**Distilled water (drops)**	**Time (s)**
1	5	20	5	
2	5	10	15	
3	3	20	7	

Small-Scale Laboratory Manual

Data Table 2			
Reaction mixture	Crystal violet (*M*)	NaOH (*M*)	Rate (*M*/s)
1			
2			
3			

1. To determine the concentrations of crystal violet, multiply the original concentration $(2 \times 10^{-4}M)$ by the number of drops used, and divide by the total number of drops of solution. For reaction #1: $2 \times 10^{-4}M \times 5$ drops/(30 drops solution) $= 3.33 \times 10^{-5}M$. Record this value in **Data Table 2.**

2. To determine the concentration of NaOH, multiply the original concentration $(1.0M)$ by the number of drops used, and divide by the total number of drops of solution.

3. Calculate the average rate for each reaction. The acidic form of crystal violet is considered to be zero at the end of the reaction, so the average rate can be calculated from the following equation.

$$\frac{[CV^+]_{final} - [CV^+]_{initial}}{time} = \frac{0 - [CV^+]_{initial}}{time}$$

4. Determine the order of reaction with respect to $[CV^+]$. Examine the rate and concentration entries in the calculations table. Reading horizontally, identify the reaction mixtures for which the values for $[CV^+]$ change but the values for the [NaOH] stay the same. Then substitute the appropriate values into the following ratio. The letters x and z represent the number of the reaction mixture.

$$\frac{Rate_x}{Rate_z} = \frac{k[CV^+]_x^n [NaOH]_x^m}{k[CV^+]_z^n [NaOH]_z^m}$$

The values for the rate constant and for [NaOH] are the same in both reactions, so the ratio reduces to the following.

$$\frac{Rate_x}{Rate_z} = \frac{[CV^+]_x^n}{[CV^+]_z^n} = \left[\frac{[CV^+]_x}{[CV^+]_z}\right]^n$$

To find the value of n, the order of reaction with respect to crystal violet, you must take the logarithm of both sides.

$$\log\left[\frac{Rate_x}{Rate_z}\right] = n \log\left[\frac{[CV^+]_x}{[CV^+]_z}\right]$$

5. Determine the order of reaction with respect to [NaOH]. Examine the rate and concentration entries in the calculations table to identify the reaction mixtures for which the values for [NaOH] change, but the values for the $[CV^+]$ stay the same. Then substitute the appropriate values into the following ratio and solve for m. The letters x and z represent the number of the reaction mixture.

$$\log\left[\frac{Rate_x}{Rate_z}\right] = m \log\left[\frac{[NaOH]_x}{[NaOH]_z}\right]$$

6. Write the general rate law for this reaction, substituting your calculated values for the superscripts *m* and *n*.

_____

_____

Analyze and Conclude

1. Thinking Critically A general rate law describes the chemistry of the slowest step in the chemical reaction studied. Acetone is iodinated in the presence of sulfuric acid according to the following chemical equation. How can you account for the absence of $[I_2]$ in the rate law? Rate $= [\text{acetone}]^1 \, [\text{HCl}]^1$

_____

_____

_____

_____

2. Interpreting Data Your values for *m* and *n* may not be whole numbers. What are some sources of error or imprecision with this experiment?

_____

_____

_____

3. Error Analysis Consider that the values for each exponent should be 1. If your values differed, calculate your percent error in determining the values of the two exponents.

_____

_____

_____

_____

Real-World Chemistry

Ethyl acetate reacts with water to form acetic acid and ethanol according to the following reaction. The rate of this reaction is much too slow to be measured, but when HCl is added as a catalyst, the rate quickens significantly. Suppose the rate of reaction doubles when the concentration of ethyl acetate doubles but is unaffected by the amount of water present.

$$CH_3C(O)OC_2H_5 \; + \; H_2O \; \rightarrow \; CH_3C(O)OH \; + \; C_2H_5OH$$
ethyl acetate   water   acetic acid   ethanol

a. Write the general rate law for the uncatalyzed reaction.

b. A catalyst increases the reaction rate by changing the rate-limiting step. Suggest a rate law for the acid-catalyzed reaction.

LAB **15** **SMALL-SCALE LABORATORY MANUAL**

Observing Equilibrium

Use with
Section 18.1

Some chemical systems are reversible; that is, they do not go to completion. Instead, they reach a point of equilibrium in which a certain ratio of the concentrations of the products to the concentrations of the reactants is constant. If more reactant particles are added to the system, the equilibrium is disturbed and the system responds by making more products, thus restoring the equilibrium ratio. Similarly, if reactant particles are removed, the products react in the reverse reaction to reform reactant particles and restore equilibrium. If the reactants and products have different colors, shifts in equilibrium can be followed by observing color changes as the system is disturbed.

In this activity, you will observe how the color of the equilibrium mixture of the following chemical system changes when common ions are added and when precipitates are formed.

$$Fe^{3+} \quad + \quad SCN^- \quad \rightleftharpoons \quad FeSCN^{2+}$$

Iron(III) ion   thiocyanate ion   iron(III) thiocyanate ion

The number of Fe^{3+} ions present in solution will increase if solid $Fe(NO_3)_3$ is added to the reaction mixture at equilibrium. This means that more $FeSCN^{2+}$ ions will form, and the reaction mixture will have a color strongly resembling the color of the $FeSCN^{2+}$ ion. Similarly, the precipitation of $Fe(OH)_3$ reduces the number of Fe^{3+} ions in solution, so $FeSCN^{2+}$ ions decompose to form more Fe^{3+} ions and SCN^- ions. The color of the solution becomes more like the color of the reactants.

Problem

How do changes in the concentration of reactant ions affect equilibrium?

Objectives

- **Observe** color changes associated with shifts in equilibrium.
- **Relate** changes in reactant concentration to the direction of shift in equilibrium.

Materials

$0.1M$ $Fe(NO_3)_3$
$0.1M$ KSCN
$1.0M$ NaOH
$0.1M$ $AgNO_3$
$Fe(NO_3)_3$
NH_4SCN
KCl
distilled water

10-mL graduated
cylinder (2)
grease pencil
droppers (2)
medium test tubes
(7)
stirring rod
test-tube rack

Safety Precautions

- Always wear safety goggles, gloves, and a lab apron.
- NH_4SCN produces cyanide fumes when in contact with acids.
- $AgNO_3$ is toxic by ingestion and will stain skin and clothes.

Pre-Lab

1. How do the concentrations of the ions of a solution change when a double-replacement reaction occurs and a precipitate forms?

2. When a pink solution is mixed with a blue solution, what is the color of the resulting mixture?

3. One milliliter of $0.1M$ HCl is added to the following equilibrium system. Identify the common ion.

   $$Co(H_2O)_6^{2+} + 4Cl^- \rightleftharpoons$$
   $$Co(H_2O)_2Cl_4^{2-} + 4H_2O$$

4. Will the equilibrium in question 3 shift toward the reactants (left) or toward the products (right)?

5. Read the entire laboratory activity. Hypothesize the direction of shift in the equilibrium system for this experiment when potassium chloride is added to the reaction mixture. Record your hypothesis in the next column.

Procedure

1. Using a graduated cylinder, measure 4 mL of $0.1M$ Fe(NO$_3$)$_3$ solution into a test tube. Record the color of the Fe^{3+} ion in **Data Table 1.**

2. In a second graduated cylinder, measure 4 mL of $0.1M$ KSCN solution. Record the color of the SCN^- ion in **Data Table 1.**

3. Pour the KSCN solution into the Fe(NO$_3$)$_3$ solution. Record the color of the $FeSCN^{2+}$ ion in **Data Table 1.**

4. Dilute the mixture to about 60 mL with water. Pour 5 mL of this *diluted* solution into each of five test tubes labeled 1–5.

5. For each step 6 through 10, record in **Data Table 2** the color of the solution after stirring, whether this color is like the products or like the reactants, the direction of shift in the equilibrium, and the identity of any common ion.

6. To test tube #1, add 0.5 g Fe(NO$_3$)$_3$. Stir to dissolve.

7. To test tube #2, add 0.5 g NH$_4$SCN. Stir to dissolve.

8. To test tube #3, add 0.5 g KCl. Stir to dissolve.

9. To test tube #4, add 3 drops of $1.0M$ NaOH solution. Stir to mix.

10. To test tube #5, add 10 drops of $0.1M$ AgNO$_3$ solution. Stir to mix.

Hypothesis

_____

_____

_____

Cleanup and Disposal

1. Dispose of all solutions as directed by your teacher.

2. Return all lab equipment to its proper place.

3. Wash your hands thoroughly with soap or detergent before you leave the lab.

Data and Observations

Data Table 1	
Substance	**Color**
Fe(NO$_3$)$_3$	
KSCN	
FeSCN^{2+} ion	

LAB 15

SMALL-SCALE LABORATORY MANUAL

				Color is most like		Equilibrium shifts toward	
Test-tube number	**Substance disturbing equilibrium**	**Common ion added**	**Color after stirring**	**Reactants**	**Products**	**Left**	**Right**
1	0.5 g $Fe(NO_3)_3$						
2	0.5 g NH_4SCN						
3	0.5 g KCl						
4	1.0M NaOH						
5	0.1M $AgNO_3$						

Data Table 2

Analyze and Conclude

1. **Observing and Inferring** Was a reactant ion or a product ion removed from the equilibrium mixture when you added NaOH and a precipitate formed?

_____

_____

_____

2. **Observing and Inferring** Based on observations, did the addition of KCl increase or decrease the reactant concentrations? (Hint: When the KCl was added to the equilibrium system, did the equilibrium shift in the same direction as it shifted for the common ion Fe^{3+}?)

_____

_____

_____

3. **Observing and Inferring** Use your data to support or refute the following statement. The precipitate formed after adding $AgNO_3$ removed SCN^- ion rather than $FeSCN^{2+}$ ion.

_____

_____

_____

4. Predicting Examine **Data Table 2** and then write a sentence to describe how the equilibrium shifts when

a. reactant ions are removed from solution.

_____

_____

_____

b. reactant ions are added to the solution.

_____

_____

_____

Real-World Chemistry

1. Manipulating an equilibrium system to achieve the desired product is a significant part of industrial chemistry. Look up the Haber process for ammonia synthesis and investigate how the conditions of the reaction are manipulated to maximize the amount of ammonia obtained.

2. Bottled carbonated beverages contain carbonic acid that dissolves in water according to the following equation: $CO_2(g) + H_2O(l) \rightleftharpoons H_2CO_3(aq)$. When a bottle is unsealed, the equilibrium is disturbed. What effect does the escaping carbon dioxide gas have on the equilibrium?

LAB **16** SMALL-SCALE LABORATORY MANUAL

Exploring Chemical Equilibrium

Use with
Section 18.2

Reversible chemical reactions reach an equilibrium in which the concentrations of all reactants and products are constant. The relationship between the reactant and product concentrations is defined by the equilibrium constant, K_{eq}. In this experiment, you will investigate the reaction in which colorless Fe^{3+} and SCN^- ions combine to form red $FeSCN^{2+}$ ions. The intensity of the red color increases with the concentration of $FeSCN^{2+}$. The net ionic equation for this reversible reaction is $Fe^{3+}(aq) + SCN^-(aq) \rightleftharpoons FeSCN^{2+}(aq)$.

Problem

Can you calculate the equilibrium constant for a chemical reaction by measuring the concentration of the reaction product?

Objectives

- **Prepare** serial dilutions of a standard solution.
- **Estimate** the color intensity of solutions at equilibrium.
- **Relate** color-intensity values to the concentration of $FeSCN^{2+}$ at equilibrium.
- **Calculate** the equilibrium constant for the reaction between Fe^{3+} and SCN^-.

Materials

$0.200M$ $Fe(NO_3)_3$

$0.6M$ HNO_3

$2.00 \times 10^{-3}M$ KSCN

24-well microplate

thin-stem pipettes (6)

sheet of white paper

Safety Precautions

- Always wear safety goggles, gloves, and a lab apron.
- Do not operate a pipette with your mouth.
- Use extra care when handling the solutions.
- Do not dispose of materials to be recycled in the sink or trash can.

Pre-Lab

1. Contrast homogenous and heterogeneous equilibria. Which type of equilibrium is represented by the reaction between Fe^{3+} and SCN^-?

2. Write the equilibrium constant expression for the reaction between Fe^{3+} and SCN^-.

3. What effect would decreasing the concentration of Fe^{3+} have on the concentration of $FeSCN^{2+}$ at equilibrium? Explain.

4. What effect would decreasing the concentration of Fe^{3+} have on the equilibrium constant? Explain.

5. Read the entire laboratory activity. Form a hypothesis about how the color intensity will vary in wells A1–A6. Explain your reasoning. Record your hypothesis on page 62.

Procedure

1. Use a pipette to place 10 drops of $Fe(NO_3)_3$ solution in well A1 of the microplate, as shown in **Figure A.** Record the Fe^{3+} concentration in **Data Table 1.**

LAB 16

SMALL-SCALE LABORATORY MANUAL

Figure A

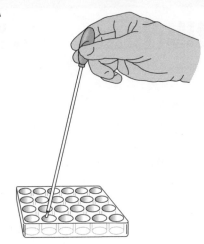

5. Repeat step 4 until you have filled all six wells in row A.

6. Add 10 drops of KSCN solution to each well in row A. Carefully stir the contents of each well.

7. Place a sheet of white paper beneath the microplate. Estimate the intensity of the red color in each well in row A on a scale from 0 (no red at all) to 1.00 (well A1). Record the intensity values in **Data Table 1.**

Hypothesis

_____

_____

_____

2. Place another 10 drops of Fe(NO$_3$)$_3$ solution in well D6. Use a second pipette to add 10 drops of HNO$_3$ solution to well D6. Stir the mixture carefully with the second pipette.

3. Transfer 10 drops of the mixture in D6 to well A2. Record the Fe^{3+} concentration in the data table. (Hint: The concentration was reduced when you added HNO$_3$ solution.)

4. Add 10 drops of HNO$_3$ solution to the mixture that remains in well D6. Stir with a clean pipette. Transfer 10 drops of this mixture to well A3. Record the Fe^{3+} concentration in **Data Table 1.**

Cleanup and Disposal

1. Dispose of all solutions as directed by your teacher.

2. Return all lab equipment to its proper place.

3. Wash your hands thoroughly with soap or detergennt before you leave the lab.

Data and Observations

Well	[Fe^{3+}] before mixing (*M*)	[Fe^{3+}] after mixing (*M*)	[SCN$^-$] after mixing (*M*)	Color intensity	[FeSCN^{2+}] at equilibrium (*M*)	[SCN$^-$] at equilibrium (*M*)	[Fe^{3+}] at equilibrium (*M*)	K_{eq}
					Data Table 1			
A1								—
A2								
A3								
A4								
A5								
A6								

LAB 16

SMALL-SCALE LABORATORY MANUAL

1. Calculate the concentration of Fe^{3+} in each well after mixing with KSCN. (Hint: Remember that 10 drops of KSCN solution was added to 10 drops of $Fe(NO_3)_3$ solution in each well.) Record the results in **Data Table 1**.

2. Calculate the concentration of SCN^- in each well after mixing. (Hint: The value will be the same for all wells.) Record the results in **Data Table 1**.

3. Calculate the concentrations of $FeSCN^{2+}$, SCN^-, and Fe^{3+} in well A1 at equilibrium. To make these calculations, assume that all of the SCN^- was consumed in the reaction in this well. Record the results in **Data Table 1**.

4. Calculate the concentration of $FeSCN^{2+}$ in wells A2–A6 at equilibrium. Multiply the equilibrium concentration in well A1 by the color intensity in each well. Record the results in **Data Table 1**.

5. Calculate the concentration of SCN^- in wells A2–A6 at equilibrium. Subtract the concentration of $FeSCN^{2+}$ at equilibrium from the concentration of SCN^- after mixing. Record the results in **Data Table 1**.

6. Calculate the concentration of Fe^{3+} in wells A2–A6 at equilibrium. Subtract the concentration of $FeSCN^{2+}$ at equilibrium from the concentration of Fe^{3+} after mixing. Record the results in **Data Table 1**.

7. Calculate the equilibrium constant, K_{eq}, using the equilibrium concentrations of $FeSCN^{2+}$, SCN^-, and Fe^{3+} in wells A2–A6. Record the results in **Data Table 1**.

Analyze and Conclude

1. **Drawing a Conclusion** Did your results support your hypothesis? Explain.

_____

_____

_____

2. **Applying Concepts** How would the results differ if the experiment was done at a higher temperature?

_____

_____

_____

_____

3. **Collecting and Interpreting Data** Based on the values you calculated for K_{eq}, do you think the procedure was precise? Explain why or why not. (Hint: Values that are within the same order of magnitude may be considered precise.)

_____

_____

_____

LAB (16) **SMALL-SCALE LABORATORY MANUAL**

4. **Error Analysis** Explain possible sources of imprecision in the experiment.

_____

_____

_____

_____

Real-World Chemistry

1. Many homes have water pipes made of iron, which can slowly release Fe^{3+} ions into the water. Although these ions are not a health hazard, at high concentrations they can discolor dishes and laundry. Explain how KSCN could be used in a home test kit for measuring the level of Fe^{3+} in water.

2. Acetic acid (CH_3COOH) and ethanol (C_2H_5OH) react to form ethyl acetate ($CH_3COOC_2H_5$) which is used to make artificial silk. Water is also produced in this reaction.

$$CH_3COOH + C_2H_5OH \rightleftharpoons CH_3COOC_2H_5 + H_2O$$

Explain why it is important to remove ethyl acetate as it forms. What other steps could be taken to increase the production of ethyl acetate?

LAB 17 SMALL-SCALE LABORATORY MANUAL

Comparing the Strengths of Acids

Use with Section 19.3

Acids ionize and produce hydrogen ions in aqueous solution. The strength of an acid depends on how completely it ionizes. Strong acids undergo essentially complete ionization, whereas weak acids are only partly ionized at equilibrium. Like other reversible reactions, the ionization of a weak acid can be represented by an equilibrium constant expression. The value of this expression, called the acid ionization constant, K_a, is a measure of the strength of a weak acid.

Problem

Can you compare the strengths of several acids by measuring the pH of their solutions and calculating K_a?

Objectives

- **Prepare** serial dilutions of standard acid solutions.
- **Measure** the pH of the standard and diluted solutions.
- **Calculate** the H$^+$ ion concentration of each solution and the K_a of each weak acid.
- **Rank** the acids in order of strength.

Materials

0.100M boric acid (H_3BO_3)
0.100M citric acid ($H_3C_6H_5O_7$)
0.100M hydrogen peroxide (H_2O_2)
0.100M permanganic acid ($HMnO_4$)
24-well microplate
thin-stem pipettes (12)
pH papers (various pH ranges)
distilled water

Safety Precautions

- Always wear safety goggles, gloves, and a lab apron.
- Use extra care when handling the solutions.
- Notify your teacher of any chemical spills.
- Do not dispose of materials to be recycled in the sink or trash can.

Pre-Lab

1. Explain the difference between the terms *weak acid* and *dilute acid*.
2. Formic acid has a K_a of 1.8×10^{-4}. Acetic acid has a K_a of 1.8×10^{-5}. Which acid is stronger? Explain your answer.
3. Define pH.
4. Read the entire laboratory activity. Form a hypothesis about the effect of decreasing the concentration of a weak acid on the pH of the acid solution and on the K_a of the acid. Record your hypothesis on page 66.
5. Write the equilibrium constant expression for this reaction: $HA(aq) \rightleftharpoons H^+(aq) + A^-(aq)$.

Procedure

1. Use a pipette to place 18 drops of distilled water in each well in columns 2 and 3 of the microplate.
2. Place about 20 drops of 0.100M boric acid in well A1. Record the name of the acid and the concentration in **Data Table 1.**
3. Transfer 2 drops of the solution in well A1 to the distilled water in well A2. Carefully stir the mixture in well A2 with the pipette.
4. Transfer 2 drops of the solution in well A2 to the distilled water in well A3. Carefully stir the mixture in well A3 with the pipette.

5. Repeat steps 2–4 with citric acid, hydrogen peroxide, and permanganic acid. Place each acid in different rows of the microplate.

6. Using pH paper, measure the pH of the solutions in wells A1–D1 and A3–D3. If a paper fails to indicate a pH value for a well, try a paper with a different pH range. Record the pH values in **Data Table 1.**

Hypothesis

_____

_____

_____

Cleanup and Disposal

1. Dispose of all solutions as directed by your teacher.

2. Return all lab equipment to its proper place.

3. Wash your hands thoroughly with soap or detergent before you leave the lab.

Data and Observations

Data Table 1							
Well	Acid	Initial [Acid] (*M*)	pH	[H$^+$] at equilibrium (*M*)	[Acid] at equilibrium (*M*)	K_a	Average K_a
A1							
A3							
B1							
B3							
C1							
C3							
D1							
D3							

1. Calculate the initial concentration of acid in wells A3–D3. (Hint: Remember that the solutions in each of these wells were made by two 10-fold dilutions of the solutions in wells A1–D1.) Record your results in **Data Table 1.**

2. Calculate the concentration of H$^+$ ions in wells A1–D1 and A3–D3 at equilibrium. (Hint: Use the formula that relates pH and [H$^+$].) Record your results.

3. Calculate the concentration of acid in wells A1–D1 and A3–D3 at equilibrium. (Hint: Subtract the concentration of H$^+$ ions at equilibrium from the initial concentration of acid.) Record your results in **Data Table 1.**

4. Calculate the acid ionization constant, K_a, for each acid, using the equilibrium concentrations of acid and H$^+$ in wells A1–D1 and A3–D3. (Hint: Remember that the concentration of the conjugate base, A$^-$, equals the concentration of H$^+$.) Record your results. If the concentration of acid at equilibrium is zero in any well, draw a dash in the K_a column for that cell.

5. Calculate the average K_a for each acid. Record your results in **Data Table 1.**

Analyze and Conclude

1. **Applying Concepts** If the concentration of acid at equilibrium is zero in any well, you can conclude that the acid in that well is a strong acid. Explain why.

_____

_____

_____

2. **Drawing a Conclusion** Rank the acids in order of strength based on your results. Indicate whether each acid is a strong or weak acid.

_____

_____

_____

3. **Error Analysis** Look up the accepted value of K_a for each weak acid. Compare the average K_a you calculated for each acid with the accepted value. Calculate the percent error if any. Explain possible sources of error in the lab.

_____

_____

_____

_____

_____

Real-World Chemistry

1. Your body contains a large number of acids, which serve a wide variety of functions. Included are 20 different kinds of amino acids, which are linked to form proteins and the nucleic acid DNA, which stores genetic information. Look up the acid ionization constants of amino acids and DNA. How do the strengths of these acids compare with those of the acids you studied in this activity?

2. The hydrangea is a popular garden shrub that produces large, round clusters of flowers. Some hydrangeas produce blue flowers when they grow in acidic soil and pink flowers when they grow in basic soil. Would it be a good idea for a gardener to fertilize a hydrangea with compost made from lemon and orange rinds if she wanted the plant to produce pink flowers? Explain your answer.

3. Acid rain is rainwater that has a pH lower than the normal value of about 5.5. It has been blamed for the corrosion of buildings and statues and for widespread environmental damage. Government regulations aimed at reducing acid rain focus mainly on limiting the release of sulfur oxides and nitrogen oxides into the air. Explain why. (Hint: Recall what you have learned about anhydrides.)

LAB 18 **SMALL-SCALE LABORATORY MANUAL**

Testing the Acidity of Aspirin

Use with
Section 19.4

Aspirin is a medicine that has been used for over a century to relieve pain, reduce fever, and fight inflammation. Aspirin is the common name for acetylsalicylic acid ($C_9H_8O_4$). Because aspirin is an acid, it can cause an upset stomach in some people who use it. Therefore, many drug companies also produce buffered aspirin, a pain reliever that is designed to be gentler on the stomach.

Problem

How can you use a base to test the difference between buffered and unbuffered aspirin?

Objectives

- **Measure** the pH of solutions of unbuffered and buffered aspirin.
- **Titrate** each solution with a base.
- **Make** and **use** a graph of pH versus volume of base for the two pain relievers.

Materials

0.1M NaOH
unbuffered aspirin
  tablet
buffered aspirin
  tablet
10-mL graduated
  cylinder

50-mL beaker
mortar and pestle
thin-stem pipettes
  (3)
stirring rod
pH paper
distilled water
plastic spoon

Safety Precautions

- Always wear safety goggles, gloves, and a lab apron.
- Use extra care when handling the solutions.
- Notify your teacher of any chemical spills.
- Do not dispose of materials to be recycled in the sink or trash can.

Pre-Lab

1. What happens in a neutralization reaction?

2. What is a buffer?

3. Suppose a buffer contains 0.1 mole of a weak acid (HA) dissolved in water. What else must the buffer contain?

4. How can you identify the equivalence point of a titration by examining a graph of pH versus volume of base added?

5. Read the entire laboratory activity. Form a hypothesis about which pain reliever will show a smaller change in pH when base is added. Explain why. Record your hypothesis on page 70.

Procedure

1. Measure 5.0 mL of distilled water in a 10-mL graduated cylinder. Remember to take the volume reading at the bottom of the meniscus.

2. Fill a pipette with distilled water. Count the number of drops that must be added from the pipette to bring the water level in the graduated cylinder to the 6.0-mL mark. Record this number in **Data Table 1**.

3. Using a mortar and pestle, grind one tablet of unbuffered aspirin into a fine powder. Transfer the ground tablet to a 50-mL beaker.

4. Add 20 mL of distilled water to the beaker. Using a stirring rod, stir the mixture until the powder is dissolved.

5. Measure the pH of the solution with pH paper. Record the pH in **Data Table 1.**

6. Use the pipette to add 1.0 mL of 0.1M NaOH to the beaker. Stir the mixture.

7. Measure the pH of the solution with pH paper. Record the pH in the data table column for each additional 1.0 mL of NaOH added.

8. Repeat steps 6 and 7 until you have added 5.0 mL of NaOH.

9. Repeat steps 3–8 using one tablet of buffered aspirin.

10. Calculate the change in pH for each pain reliever by subtracting the pH before adding NaOH from the pH after adding 5.0 mL of NaOH. Record your results in **Data Table 1.**

Hypothesis

_____

_____

_____

Cleanup and Disposal

1. Dispose of all solutions as directed by your teacher.

2. Return all lab equipment to its proper place.

3. Wash your hands thoroughly with soap or detergent before you leave the lab.

Data and Observations

Data Table 1							
Number of drops in 1.0 mL:							
Pain reliever	**pH before NaOH**	**pH after adding NaOH**					**Change in pH**
		1.0 mL	**2.0 mL**	**3.0 mL**	**4.0 mL**	**5.0 mL**	
Unbuffered aspirin							
Buffered aspirin							

Analyze and Conclude

1. Making and Using Graphs Make a graph of pH versus volume of NaOH added. Plot the data for both pain relievers on the same graph. Draw lines between the data points for each curve. Label both curves and both axes, and give the graph a title.

Small-Scale Laboratory Manual

2. Making and Using Graphs Does your graph indicate that either pain reliever was titrated to its equivalence point? Explain your answer.

_____

_____

_____

3. Collecting and Interpreting Data Which pain reliever is more acidic?

_____

4. Error Analysis Compare the results of this experiment with your hypothesis. Explain possible reasons for any disagreement.

_____

_____

_____

Real-World Chemistry

1. Scientists have discovered the remains of dead organisms in peat bogs that are well preserved after hundreds or even thousands of years. Tannic acid, a compound found in peat bogs, slows the breakdown of the dead organisms' tissues, although it usually destroys the DNA in the tissues. However, the DNA is protected from destruction if the area contains limestone, a mineral made of calcium carbonate ($CaCO_3$). Explain how calcium carbonate protects DNA. (Hint: Refer to **Table 19-2** in your textbook.)

2. Methanoic acid (HCOOH) is used in the processing of leather. To determine the concentration of methanoic acid in the process residue, chemists can titrate the residue with a base. Suppose a 75.0-mL sample of residue is neutralized by 42.0 mL of 0.200M NaOH. What is the molarity of methanoic acid in the residue? (Assume the residue contains nothing but methanoic acid and water.)

3. Solutions sold for cleaning and storing contact lenses are usually buffered. Why do you think that is so?

Name _____ Date _____ Class _____

Reduction of Manganese

Use with Section 20.2

A transfer of electrons between reactants identifies oxidation–reduction reactions. A reducing agent releases electrons that are acquired by the oxidizing agent. Permanganate ions are excellent oxidizing agents because they contain manganese atoms (Mn) with a high oxidation number. The intense color of these ions acts as an indicator that marks the end of the redox reaction in much the same way that phenolphthalein marks the end of an acid–base reaction. But, because permanganate ions decompose easily, $KMnO_4$ solutions have to be titrated against a primary standard shortly before use to get their exact concentrations. A primary standard has a known concentration. For $KMnO_4$ solutions, the primary standard is sodium oxalate, $Na_2C_2O_4$, in an aqueous solution of sulfuric acid.

In this activity, a measured amount of $Na_2C_2O_4$ is dissolved in H_2SO_4 according to the following equation:

$$H_2SO_4(aq) + Na_2C_2O_4(s) \rightarrow Na_2SO_4(aq) + H_2C_2O_4(aq).$$

This colorless solution is heated, and $KMnO_4$ is added dropwise until the solution turns faint pink. The permanganate ions react with the oxalate ions according to the following reaction:

$$5H_2C_2O_4(aq) + 2KMnO_4(aq) + 3H_2SO_4(aq) \rightarrow$$
$$10CO_2(g) + 8H_2O(l) + 2MnSO_4(aq) + K_2SO_4(aq).$$

From the mass of the $Na_2C_2O_4$, the volume of potassium permanganate solution, and the stoichiometry of the balanced chemical equation, the concentration of $KMnO_4$ can be determined.

Problem

How can a standard solution containing a reducing agent be used to find the unknown concentration of an oxidizing agent?

Objectives

- **Calculate** a value for the molarity of the $KMnO_4$ solution using stoichiometry and volume data.
- **Write** and **balance** oxidation–reduction equations.

Materials

$KMnO_4$ solution
1.0M solution of H_2SO_4
0.1 g $Na_2C_2O_4$
100-mL beaker
10-mL graduated cylinder
micropipettes (2)

test tubes (3)
thermometer
test-tube holder
test-tube rack
hot plate
grease pencil
stirring rod
distilled water

Safety Precautions

- Always wear safety glasses, gloves, and a lab apron.
- Acids can be corrosive. Handle with care.
- Sodium oxalate is toxic and an irritant.
- Potassium permanganate is toxic and an irritant.
- Never place a pipette in your mouth.

Pre-Lab

1. Write and balance the net ionic equation for the redox reaction between $KMnO_4$ and $H_2C_2O_4$.

2. What is the oxidation state of manganese in MnO_4^-? In $MnSO_4$?

3. According to the balanced equation, how many electrons are transferred?

4. Suppose that 30.00 mL of $KMnO_4$ solution exactly reacts with 0.250 g of $Na_2C_2O_4$ that has been dissolved in H_2SO_4. Calculate the molarity of the $KMnO_4$ solution.

5. Read the entire laboratory activity. If the $KMnO_4$ solution is exactly 0.04M, how many drops will be needed to react with 0.10 g $Na_2C_2O_4$? (Hint: There are 24 drops in 1 milliliter.)

6. Hypothesize about what element in the $KMnO_4$ and NaC_2O_4 is oxidized and what element is reduced. Record your hypothesis below.

Procedure

1. Fill a 100-mL beaker with distilled water. Fill one micropipette with distilled water. Count the number of drops needed to fill a 10-mL graduated cylinder to the 1.00 mL mark. Record the number of drops in **Data Table 1.** Repeat this process two more times. Label this pipette "$KMnO_4$."

2. Repeat step 1 for the second micropipette. Label this pipette "H_2SO_4."

3. Prepare a hot-water bath. Adjust the water level in the 100-mL beaker to 75 mL. Set the beaker on a hot plate and heat the water to between 80°C and 90°C. Do not boil the water. This causes the formation of a murky brown solution, and the endpoint cannot be reached.

4. Measure and record the mass of 0.10 g $Na_2C_2O_4$ to the nearest hundredth of a gram. Transfer the solid to a test tube, and set the test tube in a test-tube rack. Label a second small test tube "WASTE" and set it in the test-tube rack.

5. Rinse the calibrated H_2SO_4 micropipette with a small amount of the sulfuric acid solution. Put the H_2SO_4 rinse into the waste test tube. Partially fill the micropipette with 1.0M sulfuric

acid solution, and add 2 mL of this acid to the test tube containing the $Na_2C_2O_4$.

6. Using a test-tube holder, place the test tube containing the acidic oxalate solution into the water bath. Allow the solution to warm for 5 minutes.

7. While the test tube is warming, rinse the 10-mL graduated cylinder with $KMnO_4$. Put the $KMnO_4$ rinse into the waste test tube. Then fill the graduated cylinder with 10 mL of the $KMnO_4$ solution.

8. Fill a third test tube halfway with distilled water. Rinse the $KMnO_4$ micropipette with a small amount of the potassium permanganate solution. Put the $KMnO_4$ rinse into the waste test tube. Partially fill the micropipette with $KMnO_4$ solution from the graduated cylinder, and add 1 drop to the test tube containing distilled water. This is your titration standard; it is the color of the reaction mixture at the endpoint.

9. Using the $KMnO_4$ micropipette, add 3 drops of the $KMnO_4$ solution into the test tube warming in the water bath. Keep the test tube in the water bath. Stir until the color disappears (5 minutes or less).

10. After the color disappears, keep the temperature of the water bath above 65°C and continue to add drops of $KMnO_4$ one at a time while stirring constantly. Add drops of $KMnO_4$ until the added drop turns the solution the same pink color as the titration standard. The color should persist for 30 s. Record the total number of drops in **Data Table 2.**

Hypothesis

_____

_____

Cleanup and Disposal

1. Dispose of all chemicals as directed by your teacher.

2. Return all lab equipment to its proper place.

3. Wash your hands thoroughly with soap or detergent before you leave the lab.

LAB 19

SMALL-SCALE LABORATORY MANUAL

Data and Observations

Data Table 1				
Micropipette used for:	**Number of drops in 1 mL**			
	Trial 1	**Trial 2**	**Trial 3**	**Average**
$KMnO_4$				
H_2SO_4				

Data Table 2	
Mass of sodium oxalate (g)	
Drops of $KMnO_4$ needed to reach endpoint	
Volume of $KMnO_4$ needed to reach endpoint (mL)	

1. Calculate the average number of drops in 1 milliliter for your micropipettes. Record this number in **Data Table 1.**

2. Multiply the drops of $KMnO_4$ needed to reach endpoint by the average number of drops per milliliter to calculate the volume of the $KMnO_4$ solution used. Record this number in **Data Table 2.**

3. Calculate the molar mass of sodium oxalate and record the mass in **Data Table 2.**

4. Calculate the number of moles of sodium oxalate.

5. Using the balanced chemical equation and the number of moles of the $Na_2C_2O_4$, calculate the number of moles of $KMnO_4$ used.

6. Divide the number of moles of $KMnO_4$ (from question 5) by the volume of $KMnO_4$ (from question 2). This is the exact molarity, the standardized concentration.

Analyze and Conclude

1. **Observing and Inferring** What is the purpose of calibrating the micropipette?

_____

_____

2. **Observing and Inferring** What color was the solution containing H_2SO_4 and $Na_2C_2O_4$? Containing $KMnO_4$? Use the balanced net ionic equation to infer why the pink color occurs at the endpoint.

_____

_____

_____

_____

3. **Error Analysis** Explain possible sources of error in this activity.

_____

_____

_____

_____

Real-World Chemistry

1. Chlorine is used as a bleach and disinfectant, but totally dry chlorine has no bleaching power. Chlorine owes its bleaching capability to the hypochlorous acid, HClO, that is formed when chlorine reacts with water. Once the HClO is formed, it readily gives up oxygen, O, to any nearby oxidizable substance. The following chemical equations describe these two reactions:

a. $Cl_2 + H_2O \rightarrow HCl + HClO$

b. $HClO \rightarrow HCl + O$

Would you expect the bleaching action of HClO to be the result of its activity as an oxidizing agent or a reducing agent? Explain your reasoning.

2. Manganese dioxide is a decomposition product of the permanganate ion. It is also part of the cathode in an alkaline flashlight battery. Examine the cathodic half-reaction:

$2MnO_2(s) + H_2O(l) \rightarrow Mn_2O_3(s) + 2OH^-(aq)$

Is MnO_2 an oxidizing agent or a reducing agent? Which process takes place at the cathode—oxidation or reduction?

LAB 20 SMALL-SCALE LABORATORY MANUAL

Plants Produce Oxygen

Use with Section 26.4

An ecosystem is the sum total of all organisms and their environments within a given area. For most ecosystems, sunlight is the ultimate energy source. Green plants, algae, and some bacteria absorb the energy from the red, blue, and indigo wavelengths of the sunlight. The light energy facilitates the production of oxygen and carbohydrates from carbon dioxide and water.

$$6CO_2 + 6H_2O \xrightarrow[\text{chlorophyll enzymes}]{\text{light energy}} C_6H_{12}O_6 + 6O_2$$

This conversion process, photosynthesis, was observed by Priestley in 1772. He observed that when a plant and an animal were kept together in an airtight jar, both lived; but when kept separately, both died. Later, investigators realized that the plants produce oxygen, while the animal exhales carbon dioxide and water vapor. To be complete, this mini-ecosystem requires complimentary processes.

Researchers discovered that the energy needed for photosynthesis was obtained from the red and blue wavelengths of light absorbed by green chloroplasts in plant leaves. Oxygen production in the chloroplasts of algae then led scientists to hypothesize that photosynthesis took place in the chloroplasts. Because oxygen gas is a product of photosynthesis, monitoring its production is an indirect measure of the amount of photosynthesis.

In this activity, you will prepare two test samples containing an indicator and different amounts of CO_2. As CO_2 is consumed to produce oxygen, the color of the solution changes. By observing how quickly the color change occurs, you can qualitatively evaluate the dependence of photosynthesis on carbon dioxide concentration. Because oxygen gas is colorless and odorless at room temperature and pressure, methylene blue is used as an indicator. Oxygen gas is the only gas that removes the color from methylene blue.

Problem

How does carbon dioxide concentration affect the rate of photosynthesis?

Objectives

- **Observe** the production of oxygen gas using an indicator.
- **Relate** the rate of oxygen production to carbon dioxide concentration.
- **Infer** the effect of carbon dioxide concentration on photosynthesis.

Materials

0.2% sodium hydrogen carbonate ($NaHCO_3$) solution
methylene blue indicator solution
green leaves
plastic weighing cup

micropipettes (2)
small test tubes (3)
scissors
scoop or equivalent
stirring rod
test-tube rack
distilled water
light source

Chemistry: Matter and Change • Chapter 26 **77**

SMALL-SCALE LABORATORY MANUAL

Safety Precautions

- **Always wear safety goggles, gloves, and a lab apron.**
- **Methylene blue will stain skin and clothing.**
- **Never place the pipette in your mouth.**

Pre-Lab

1. Read the entire laboratory activity. Sodium hydrogen carbonate dissolved in water is a source of CO_2. The chemical equation for photosynthesis shows the relationship between CO_2 and O_2. Form a hypothesis as to which substance—$NaHCO_3$ or distilled water—will cause photosynthesis to occur more rapidly. Record your hypothesis in the next column.

2. Read a biology book to learn what chloroplasts are and where they are found. What is their function?

3. What is the purpose of a test tube with distilled water but no leaf pieces?

4. When methylene blue loses its color, what gas is present? Explain.

Procedure

1. Using a micropipette, fill two small test tubes half full with distilled water and set the tubes in a test-tube rack. Fill a third small test tube half full with 0.2% sodium hydrogen carbonate solution and set it in the test-tube rack. Add 3 drops of methylene blue solution to each test tube.

2. Using the scissors, cut a green leaf into pieces small enough to fit into the test tubes. Collect the pieces in the plastic weighing cup.

3. Using a scoop, divide the leaf pieces between one of the test tubes filled with distilled water and the test tube filled with sodium hydrogen carbonate solution. Be sure to add the same quantity of leaves to each test tube.

4. Using a stirring rod, mix the leaves into each solution. (Leaves may remain near the surface of the liquid.) Then place the three test tubes in a sunny window or under a lamp.

5. Record your observations of the solutions in the *0 min* column of **Data Table 1.**

6. Record your observations of the solutions at 1-min intervals until the solution decolorizes. (More entries may be needed if the day is cloudy.)

Hypothesis

_____

_____

_____

_____

_____

Cleanup and Disposal

1. Dispose of all chemicals as directed by your teacher.

2. Return all lab equipment to its proper place.

3. Wash your hands thoroughly with soap or detergent before you leave the lab.

LAB 20

Data and Observations

Data Table 1							
	Time elapsed (min)						
Solution	0	1	2	3	4	5	6
Distilled water + methylene blue							
Distilled water + leaf pieces + methylene blue							
Na_2HCO_3 solution + leaf pieces + methylene blue							

Analyze and Conclude

1. **Observing and Inferring** Which test tube better supports photosynthesis? Support your answer with evidence from your observations.

   _____

   _____

   _____

   _____

2. **Drawing a Conclusion** What is the relationship between CO_2 concentration and the rate of photosynthesis?

   _____

   _____

   _____

3. **Measuring and Using Numbers** Starch is the storage carbohydrate in plants. Starch is a polymer of glucose molecules that were formed during photosynthesis. Suppose 5 mL of O_2 gas is produced during a photosynthesis experiment similar to this one. If the gas was collected at 22.0°C and a barometric pressure of 754 mm Hg, what mass of glucose ($C_6H_{12}O_6$) was produced? (Hint: $PV = nRT$; replace the general carbohydrate formula in the photosynthesis equation with the formula for glucose.)

LAB ⟨20⟩   **SMALL-SCALE LABORATORY MANUAL**

4. Designing an Experiment/Identifying Variables How could the experimental design be modified to collect and measure the amount of O_2 gas produced?

_____

_____

_____

_____

_____

_____

5. Error Analysis Explain possible sources of error in this activity.

_____

_____

_____

_____

Real-World Chemistry

1. Greenbelts are narrow areas of trees, shrubs, and other greenery that are planted around a community. Automobiles are propelled by the combustion of fossil fuels. Why is it important to have greenbelts along major freeways?

2. Oxygen promotes deterioration of food products. One patented indicator for detecting oxygen in food packaging includes methylene blue in its formulation. For what reason would methylene blue be included? What advantage might it have over other indicators?

SMALL-SCALE LABORATORY MANUAL
Teacher Guide

Lab 1 Small-Scale Laboratory Techniques

Use with Section 2.1

Objectives
▶ Measure the mass of a piece of candy.
▶ Measure the volume of a small amount of water.
▶ Dissolve the candy in the water.
▶ Use a pipette and a microplate to make serial dilutions of the candy-water solution.

Process Skills
Collecting and interpreting data, making and using tables, measuring and using numbers, observing and inferring, thinking critically

Time Allotment
1 class period

Materials
See pages 11T–14T for materials.
(Visit the Chemistry Web site at **science.glencoe.com** *to find links about safety in the laboratory.)*

Alternative Materials
▶ The lab exercise describes how to use a beam balance; an electronic balance may be used instead.
▶ LifeSavers® or any other small, water-soluble, colored candies may be used.

Preparation
▶ Make sure the balances are in good working order before students begin the lab.
▶ Each group of students needs one piece of candy, but extra candy should be available so that students can repeat a procedure if they make a mistake.

Pre-Lab
1. The kilogram is the SI base unit for mass.
2. Volume is measured in milliliters.
3. There are 1000 mL in 1 L. There 20 mL in 20 cm³.

Teaching the Lab
Have students work in groups of two.
▶ Explain the use of the electronic balance if one is used instead of a beam balance. The tare feature on an electronic balance can automatically subtract the mass of the beaker, but you may prefer to have students make this calculation themselves.

▶ Warn students never to place any chemicals directly on the balance pan. Explain that all chemicals should be placed either on paper or in a container such as a beaker.
▶ Emphasize that the candy used in this laboratory exercise should be treated like any other lab chemical. Remind students that they should never place any lab materials in their mouth, even if those materials may be eaten as food under other circumstances.
▶ Caution students to never place the pipette in their mouth.
▶ Explain how to estimate intermediate values of mass and volume by interpolating between marked values.
▶ Ask students why it is important that they try to make all drops from the pipette the same size. (The dilution ratios will be unknown if the drops vary in size.)

Data and Observations Sample Data

Data Table 1	
Mass of beaker (g)	55.6 g
Mass of beaker + candy (g)	57.9 g
Mass of candy (g)	2.3 g
Volume of water (mL)	19.8 mL

Analyze and Conclude
1. See "Mass of candy" row in data table.
2. Answers will depend on the measured values. For the sample values shown in the table, concentration = 2.3 g/19.8 mL = 0.12 g/mL.
3. The concentration of the diluted solution is one-tenth that of the undiluted solution. For the values shown in the table, concentration = 0.012 g/mL.
4. The number of dilutions needed to produce a colorless solution may vary. For each dilution that is performed, the concentration is reduced by a factor of 10.

Real-World Chemistry
(0.015 L)/(0.95 L + 0.015 L) × 10% = 0.14%

Lab 2 Comparing the Density of Metals

Use with Section 3.1

Objectives

▶ Measure the mass and volume of four metal samples.

▶ Calculate the density of each sample from these measurements.

▶ Compare the calculated densities with known densities of specific metals.

▶ Identify each metal sample.

Process Skills

Measuring and using numbers, making and using tables, collecting and interpreting data, applying concepts, drawing a conclusion, thinking critically

Time Allotment

1 class period

Materials

See pages 11T–14T for materials.

(Visit the Chemistry Web site at **science.glencoe.com** *to find links about safety in the laboratory.)*

Alternative Materials

Depending on availability, other metals could be used in addition to or instead of aluminum, copper, iron, and lead. For example, sinkers made of tin may be purchased from fishing tackle stores.

Preparation

▶ Place different metal samples in separate boxes labeled A, B, C, and D. Make a note that A = lead, B = iron, C = aluminum, and D = copper.

▶ Be sure that the mass of each sample does not exceed the maximum allowed mass for the laboratory balances.

Pre-Lab

1. Density = mass/volume. Accept any SI units of mass divided by volume, such as g/cm^3 or g/mL.

2. Base units are based on objects or events in the physical world and are independent of other units. Derived units are defined by a combination of base units.

3. derived units

4. Density = mass/volume = 85.6 g/12.1 mL = 7.07 g/mL.

5. Volume = mass/density = $(50.0 \times 10^3 \text{ g})/(19.3 \text{ g/mL})$ = 2.59×10^3 mL = 2.59 L.

Teaching the Lab

Have students work in groups of two.

▶ Warn students to be sure that each metal sample is dry before they measure its mass.

▶ Caution students not to drop the metal sample against the side of the graduated cylinder so as not to break the cylinder.

▶ You may discuss guidelines for deciding how closely calculated densities must agree with accepted values for positive identification of samples.

▶ Caution students not to adjust their measurements or calculations in an attempt to eliminate discrepancies between calculated densities and accepted values. Have students focus instead on proposing plausible explanations for such discrepancies.

Data and Observations

See data table.

1. See "Volume of Sample" column in data table.

2. See "Density" column in data table.

Analyze and Conclude

1. Densities in g/mL at 25°C: aluminum, 2.7; copper, 8.9; iron, 7.9; lead, 11.3; tin, 7.3; tungsten, 19.3; zinc, 7.1.

Data and Observations (Lab 2)

Sample Data

Data Table 1					
Sample	Mass (g)	Volume of Water (mL)	Volume of Water + Sample (mL)	Volume of Sample (mL)	Density (g/mL)
A	123.17	27.6	38.5	10.9	11.3
B	127.53	22.4	38.6	16.2	7.87
C	15.93	29.3	35.2	5.9	2.7
D	65.86	25.5	32.9	7.4	8.9

2. A is lead, B is iron, C is aluminum, and D is copper.

3. Yes; bubbles occupy volume, so they would make the volume of the metal sample appear larger than it actually was. Thus, the calculated density of the sample would be lower than the actual density.

4. Answers may vary. One way would be to repeat the density test with greater precision to determine whether the density was closer to 7.1 g/mL or 7.3 g/mL. Another way would be to compare other properties of the sample, such as color, hardness, and heat conductivity, with known properties of tin and zinc.

5. Answers may vary. Students may have made inaccurate mass or volume measurements. Air bubbles may have been present in the water. Samples may have been alloys rather than pure metals.

Real-World Chemistry

1. The person who has 30 percent body fat should float higher in the water. Because fatty tissue is less dense than water, it tends to float on water. Therefore, the more fatty tissue a person has, the higher they will float.

2. To fly, airplanes must be lightweight. Aluminum and titanium have low densities, so a given volume of these metals will have less mass than the same volume of higher-density metals.

3. Brass should have a lower density than pure copper. Adding zinc (density 7.1 g/mL) to copper (density 8.9 g/mL) should produce an alloy that has an intermediate density.

Lab 3 Separation of Aspirin

Use with Section 3.3

Objectives

▶ Separate an aspirin tablet into two phases.

▶ Test each phase for the presence of starch.

▶ Test one of the phases for the presence of salicylic acid.

▶ Compare the amount of salicylic acid in new and old aspirin tablets.

Process Skills

Applying concepts, collecting and interpreting data, comparing and contrasting, drawing a conclusion, hypothesizing, making and using tables, observing and inferring, thinking critically

Time Allotment

1 class period

Materials

See pages 11T–14T for materials.
(Visit the Chemistry Web site at **science.glencoe.com** *to find links about safety in the laboratory.)*

Alternative Materials

Old aspirin tablets can be ones that have been stored for several months in an open container in a warm environment. You may accelerate the aging process by placing newly purchased tablets on a plate in a warm oven for several hours.

Preparation

▶ Iodine solution and iron(III) nitrate solution may be prepared months in advance.

▶ Place new aspirin tablets in a container labeled "A" and old aspirin tablets in a container labeled "B."

Pre-Lab

1. A heterogeneous mixture does not blend smoothly throughout; a homogeneous mixture has a constant composition throughout.

2. sand and water: heterogeneous; salt and water, nitrogen and oxygen in air: homogeneous

3. filtration

4. distillation

5. See Hypothesis.

Teaching the Lab

Have students work in groups of two.

▶ Caution students that isopropyl alcohol and iodine solution can irritate the eyes and respiratory tract.

▶ Demonstrate the proper use of the mortar and pestle. Instruct students to break up each tablet by gently pounding it before beginning to grind it.

▶ Remind students to try to make all drops from the pipette the same size. Explain that, for a fair comparison of the color in wells A3 and B3, the wells should contain the same volume of fluid.

▶ Caution students to never place the pipette in their mouth.

Hypothesis

Old aspirin tablets will contain more salicylic acid than new aspirin tablets. As the tablets age, more of the aspirin they contain is converted into salicylic acid and acetic acid.

Data and Observations

Sample Data

Data Table 1	
Well	Observations
A1	Solid material turns blue-black.
A2	No change in the color of the liquid.
A3	Liquid turns violet.
B1	Solid material turns blue-black.
B2	No change in the color of the liquid.
B3	Liquid turns violet, darker than liquid in A3.

Analyze and Conclude

1. A heterogeneous mixture results. The components of the mixture (the solid material and the clear liquid) are not blended smoothly throughout the mixture.

2. The solid materials in wells A1 and B1 do not dissolve in isopropyl alcohol. This material contains starch because it turns blue-black when exposed to iodine solution. Therefore, starch does not dissolve in isopropyl alcohol.

3. Wells A3 and B3 contain substances that dissolve in isopropyl alcohol. These wells contain salicylic acid because iron(III) nitrate solution turns violet when added to the wells. Therefore, salicylic acid dissolves in isopropyl alcohol.

4. The tablet from group B contains more salicylic acid because the solution in well B3 turned a darker violet color than the solution in well A3.

5. Tablet A is the new tablet; tablet B is the old tablet.

6. Answers may vary. Results should agree with the hypothesis. However, if the old tablets were not old enough, the difference between their salicylic acid content and that of the new tablets may not have been detectable by the test that was used.

Real-World Chemistry

1. Because gold is so much more dense than sand or gravel, any gold that is present will settle to the bottom of the pan, while the water carries the sand or gravel away.

2. Water is allowed to evaporate from the seawater, and as it does, the sodium chloride comes out of solution and crystallizes.

3. For example, recyclers can use a magnet to separate aluminum cans from cans made of iron because iron is magnetic, but aluminum is not.

Lab 4 Periodicity and the Properties of Elements

Use with Section 7.1

Objectives

▶ Prepare serial dilutions of solutions containing ions of alkaline earth metals.

▶ Observe precipitates that form when other chemicals are added to these solutions.

▶ Recognize patterns of solubility for compounds containing alkaline earth metals.

Process Skills

Applying concepts, collecting and interpreting data, drawing a conclusion, hypothesizing, measuring and using numbers, observing and inferring

Time Allotment

1 class period

Materials

See pages 11T–14T for materials.

(Visit the Chemistry Web site at **science.glencoe.com** *to find links about safety in the laboratory.)*

Alternative Materials

▶ If a specific compound mentioned in the materials list cannot be obtained, you may substitute another, provided the concentration of the active ion is the same.

▶ Beryllium compounds are not recommended for this activity because they are highly toxic.

Preparation

▶ Be careful with crystals of nitrates—they are strong oxidizers.

▶ Make three copies of the 96-well template for each student.

▶ All ionic solutions are $0.1M$. Use distilled water to prepare all $0.1M$ solutions.

▶ To reduce the number of pipettes required, provide a labeled pipette with each solution. Warn students not to contaminate pipettes with other solutions.

Pre-Lab

1. Elements in the same group have the same number of valence electrons.

2. Elements in the same group have different numbers of nonvalence electrons. As a result, the elements have different atomic radii and, therefore, different ionization energies.

3. Reactivity increases as atomic number increases.

4. The alkaline earth metals are beryllium, magnesium, calcium, strontium, barium, and radium.

5. See Hypothesis.

Teaching the Lab

Have students work in groups of two.

▶ Barium compounds are toxic. Remind students to follow proper chemical hygiene procedures and to wash their hands thoroughly with soap or detergent after they complete this laboratory activity.

▶ Emphasize that students should try to make all drops from the pipette the same size.

▶ If students think they may have made a mistake in preparing the serial dilution of one of the alkaline earth metal solutions, have them repeat the dilution series for that solution in another row on the microplate.

▶ Encourage students to examine the wells carefully for the presence of precipitate.

▶ Caution students to never place the pipette in their mouth.

Hypothesis

Two hypotheses are acceptable: solubility increases from compounds containing magnesium to those containing barium, or solubility decreases from compounds containing magnesium to those containing barium.

Data and Observations

Gray boxes indicate wells with precipitate.

Template 1 Precipitates Formed by Adding Na_2SO_4

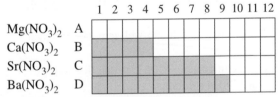

Template 2 Precipitates Formed by Adding $Na_2C_2O_4$

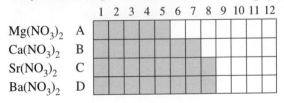

Template 3 Precipitates Formed by Adding Na_2CO_3

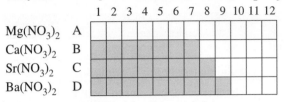

Analyze and Conclude

1. The concentration in each well was twice that in the next well to the right.

2. In reactions with Na_2SO_4 and Na_2CO_3, barium formed precipitates in wells with the lowest concentration; in reactions with $Na_2C_2O_4$, strontium and barium did so.

3. In reactions with Na_2SO_4 and Na_2CO_3, magnesium did not form precipitates at any concentration.

4. In general, solubility decreases from magnesium to barium.

5. Answers may vary. Assuming students predicted a decrease in solubility from magnesium to barium, disagreements with that hypothesis may have resulted from mixtures that contained the wrong solutions, errors in labeling the wells, inaccuracy in counting drops or in delivering drops of uniform size, or failure to observe small amounts of precipitates.

Real-World Chemistry

1. Calcium would contribute more to such deposits. The results from the addition of Na_2CO_3 indicate that combining calcium ions with carbonate ions produces a compound that is much less soluble in water than the compound formed by combining magnesium ions with carbonate ions.

2. Beryllium and aluminum have a diagonal relationship and, therefore, compounds that contain them have similar chemical properties. This makes it difficult to separate beryllium from aluminum.

3. Radium could be used because it is the only alkaline earth metal that is naturally radioactive.

Lab 5 Properties of Transition Metals

Use with Section 7.3

Objectives

▶ Observe the physical properties of ten metal ions in aqueous solution.

▶ Observe the results of mixing three chemicals with each of the solutions.

▶ Compare the chemical reactivity of transition metal ions with that of other metal ions.

Process Skills

Applying concepts, collecting and interpreting data, comparing and contrasting, hypothesizing, making and using tables, observing and inferring, recognizing cause and effect, thinking critically

Time Allotment

1 class period

Materials

See pages 11T–14T for materials.

*(Visit the Chemistry Web site at **science.glencoe.com** to find links about safety in the laboratory.)*

Alternative Materials

▶ Other transition metal compounds should be avoided because many transition metals have multiple oxidation states. Compounds in which the metals have different oxidation states will give different results.

▶ Changing the concentrations of any of the solutions used in the experiment may give different results.

Preparation

▶ Make a copy of the 96-well template for each group of students.

▶ To reduce the number of pipettes required, provide a labeled pipette with each solution. Warn students not to contaminate pipettes with other solutions.

Pre-Lab

1. Transition metals are elements whose final electron enters a d sublevel.

2. The metals are potassium, calcium, vanadium, chromium, manganese, iron, cobalt, nickel, copper, and zinc.

3. group 1A metal: potassium; group 1B metal: calcium; transition metals: vanadium, chromium, manganese, iron, cobalt, nickel, copper, and zinc

4. See Hypothesis. Potassium and calcium are not transition metals. Zinc is a transition metal, but, unlike the other transition metals tested, it has 3d and 4s orbitals that are completely filled.

Teaching the Lab

Have students work in groups of two.

▶ Caution students that several of the solutions are poisonous, that HCl is very corrosive, and that HCl and NH_3 will irritate the eyes, skin, and respiratory tract. Warn students not to mix HCl and KSCN—the combination will emit toxic cyanide fumes.

▶ Instruct students to clean up all spills immediately.

▶ Encourage students to examine the wells carefully for the presence of precipitate and for subtle color changes.

▶ If students think they may have made a mistake with a mixture, have them repeat the mixture in another well.

▶ Students may notice that two metals in period 4, scandium and titanium, are not tested in this experiment. Explain that these metals were excluded because of the high cost of compounds that contain them.

Hypothesis

Potassium, calcium, and zinc ions will have properties that are most different from those of the other metals' ions.

Data and Observations

See data table.

1. See "Color of solution" column in data table.

2. See "NH_3," "KSCN," and "HCl" columns in data table.

Analyze and Conclude

1. Precipitates formed when NH_3 was added to $Cr(NO_3)_3$, $Mn(NO_3)_2$, $Fe(NO_3)_3$, and $Co(NO_3)_3$.

2. No, it does not mean a reaction did not occur. Reactions can cause a solution to change color without forming a precipitate.

3. KNO_3, $Ca(NO_3)_2$, and $Zn(NO_3)_2$ did not appear to react with any of the other chemicals.

4. Answers may vary. Errors may have resulted from mixtures that contained the wrong solutions, errors in labeling the wells, or failure to observe faint precipitates or subtle color changes in solutions.

Data and Observations (Lab 5)   Sample Data

Data Table 1				
Metallic solution	**Color of solution**	**Effect of adding other chemicals**		
		NH₃	**KSCN**	**HCl**
KNO_3	colorless	none	none	none
$Ca(NO_3)_2$	colorless	none	none	none
NH_4VO_3	yellow	orange	pale green	none
$Cr(NO_3)_3$	purple	green precipitate	violet	violet
$Mn(NO_3)_2$	light rose	white precipitate	none	none
$Fe(NO_3)_3$	dark yellow	brown precipitate	red	orange
$Co(NO_3)_2$	pink	green precipitate	violet	pink
$Ni(NO_3)_2$	emerald green	pale blue	pale green	light green
$Cu(NO_3)_2$	blue	blue	green	green
$Zn(NO_3)_2$	colorless	none	none	none

Real-World Chemistry

1. Zinc would be easiest to separate because its boiling point (907°C) is much lower than the boiling points of the other period 4 transition metals.

2. Cobalt chloride ink on heated paper would appear blue. In this experiment, a blue mixture containing cobalt chloride was formed when HCl was added to $Co(NO_3)_2$ solution.

3. Products such as these must be made of alloys that are extremely strong and, in some cases, heat resistant. Most transition metals are extremely hard and have high melting points, and they impart these properties to alloys that contain them.

Lab 6 Modeling Molecular Shapes

Use with Section 9.4

Objectives

▶ Construct models of molecules by using inflated balloons.
▶ Observe how varying the number of covalent bonds and lone pairs of electrons affects molecular shape.

Process Skills

Applying concepts, formulating models, hypothesizing, making and using tables, observing and inferring, predicting, thinking critically

Time Allotment

1 class period

Materials

See pages 11T–14T for materials.

(Visit the Chemistry Web site at **science.glencoe.com** *to find links about safety in the laboratory.)*

Alternative Materials

▶ Do not use balloons that inflate to shapes other than round or pear-shaped.
▶ Do not use double-sided tape to connect the balloons, as it does not have the flexibility of tape loops and will result in a large number of broken balloons.

Preparation

Have plastic-foam model materials available for students who wish to extend beyond this activity and model more complex molecules.

Pre-Lab

1. A covalent bond involves the sharing of valence electrons between two atoms; an ionic bond involves the transfer of one or more electrons from one atom to another.

2. The model predicts a shape that minimizes the repulsion of shared and unshared pairs of electrons around a central atom.

3. Lone pairs push shared bonding orbitals together slightly because lone pairs occupy a slightly larger orbital than do shared electrons.

4. Hybridization is the mixing of atomic orbitals to form new, identical orbitals.

5. See Hypothesis.

Teaching the Lab

Have students work in groups of two.

▶ Ask students if they have known allergic reactions to latex, of which the balloons are made.

▶ Demonstrate repulsion of electron pairs by rubbing two inflated pear-shaped balloons against an article of clothing and bringing the balloons near each other. Rubbing gives the balloons a surface charge that should cause them to repel each other. Students may find that the shapes of their balloon models more closely match the expected shapes if the balloons carry a surface charge.

▶ Make sure students understand that the balloons represent electron orbitals, not atoms. In the case of the round balloons, the atom is at the center of the balloon. In the case of the pear-shaped balloons, the atom is at the place where two such balloons are tied together.

Hypothesis

Molecules made of two or three atoms with no lone pairs of electrons will be linear, molecules made of four atoms with no lone pairs of electrons will be trigonal planar, and molecules made of five atoms with no lone pairs of electrons will be tetrahedral.

Data and Observations

Sample Data

Data Table 1		
Molecule	**Shape**	**Bond angle (°)**
H_2	linear	180°
$BeCl_2$	linear	180°
$AlCl_3$	trigonal planar	120°
CH_4	tetrahedral	109.5°
H_2O	bent	107.3°

See "Bond Angle" column in data table.

Analyze and Conclude

1. A round balloon represents an s orbital. A pear-shaped balloon represents a p orbital.

2. $BeCl_2$, sp; $AlCl_3$, sp²; CH_4, sp³; H_2O, sp³. (No hybrid orbitals are formed in H_2.)

3. $BeCl_2$ and H_2O do not have the same shape. The central atom (beryllium) in $BeCl_2$ has no lone pairs of electrons, so $BeCl_2$ is linear; the central atom (oxygen) in H_2O has two lone pairs of electrons, so H_2O has a bent tetrahedral shape.

4. CH_3Cl, tetrahedral; Cl_2, linear; CCl_4, tetrahedral; HCl, linear; BF_3, trigonal planar

5. Answers may vary. Results should agree with the hypothesis. Disagreements may have resulted from tying the pear-shaped balloons too tightly and thus forcing the models into shapes that do not accurately represent the shapes of real molecules.

Real-World Chemistry

1. Ethene is planar with bond angles of 120°. Ethyne is linear with bond angles of 180°.

2. The part of hemoglobin that consists of iron and the atoms it bonds with is octahedral.

3. No; the tetrahedral arrangement of atoms around each carbon atom and the existence of bonds between carbon atoms make a large variety of shapes possible. Beryllium, in contrast, can form bonds with only two other atoms, so the structures it forms are linear.

Lab 7 Solutions and Precipitates

Use with Section 10.3

Objectives

▶ Write ionic equations for mixtures of aqueous solutions.
▶ Predict which mixtures will form precipitates.
▶ Observe mixtures for precipitate formation.

Process Skills

Applying concepts, collecting and interpreting data, hypothesizing, making and using tables, observing and inferring, predicting, thinking critically

Time Allotment

1 class period

Materials

See pages 11T–14T for materials.
(Visit the Chemistry Web site at **science.glencoe.com** *to find links about safety in the laboratory.)*

Alternative Materials

▶ Other aqueous solutions of ionic compounds and other mixtures of solutions may be used. Consult the *CRC Handbook of Chemistry and Physics* for information on the solubility of products of other double-replacement reactions.

▶ Reactions may be carried out in test tubes instead of microscale reaction plates.

Preparation

▶ Each group of students will need at least 20 mL of KI solution; 15 mL of $CuSO_4$, $NaCO_3$, and NaOH solutions; 10 mL of $BaCl_2$, NaCl, Na_2SO_4, and $Pb(NO_3)_2$ solutions; and 5 mL of $FeCl_3$ solution. Prepare enough of each solution so that students can repeat a mixture if they make a mistake.

▶ To reduce the number of pipettes required, provide a labeled 5 mL pipette with each solution. Warn students not to contaminate pipettes with other solutions.

Pre-Lab

1. A double-replacement reaction is a reaction involving the exchange of positive ions between two compounds dissolved in water.

2. The products are a precipitate, water, or a gas.

3. A spectator ion is an ion that does not participate in a reaction.

4. A complete ionic equation shows all of the particles in a solution, whereas a net ionic equation shows only the particles that participate in the reaction.

5. Mixtures 1, 2, 5, 6, 7, 8, and 10 will form a precipitate. These mixtures produce ionic compounds that are insoluble or partially soluble in water.

Teaching the Lab

Have students work in groups of two.

▶ Caution students that several of the solutions are poisonous and that NaOH will irritate the eyes, skin, and respiratory tract. Be certain that eyewash is accessible.

▶ Advise students to keep a careful record of which mixtures are in which wells. If students think they may have made a mistake with a mixture, have them repeat the mixture in another well.

▶ Explain that reactions that yield a partially soluble product may not produce as much precipitate as other reactions. Remind students to examine the wells carefully for the presence of precipitate.

▶ Caution students to never place the pipette in their mouth.

Hypothesis

Mixtures 1, 2, 5, 6, 7, 8, and 10 will form a precipitate.

Data and Observations (Lab 7)

Data Table 1			
Mixture	**Solutions**	**Well**	**Observations**
1	$CuSO_4$ and NaOH	1A	precipitate
2	$FeCl_3$ and NaOH	2A	precipitate
3	KI and NaOH	3A	no precipitate
4	KI and NaCl	4A	no precipitate
5	KI and $Pb(NO_3)_2$	5A	precipitate
6	Na_2SO_4 and $Pb(NO_3)_2$	6A	precipitate
7	Na_2SO_4 and $BaCl_2$	1B	precipitate
8	$NaCO_3$ and $BaCl_2$	2B	precipitate
9	$NaCO_3$ and KI	3B	no precipitate
10	$NaCO_3$ and $CuSO_4$	4B	precipitate
11	NaCl and $CuSO_4$	5B	no precipitate

Data and Observations

See data table.

1. See "Observations" column in Data Table 1.
2. No other reaction signs should be visible in any of the wells.

Analyze and Conclude

1. Mixtures 1, 2, 5, 6, 7, 8, and 10 should have resulted in a reaction. The presence of a precipitate in those mixtures showed that a reaction occurred.

2. $Cu^{2+}(aq) + SO_4^{2-}(aq) + 2Na^+(aq) + 2OH^-(aq) \rightarrow$
   $Cu(OH)_2(s) + 2Na^+(aq) + SO_4^{2-}(aq)$

   $Fe^{3+}(aq) + 3Cl^-(aq) + 3Na^+(aq) + 3OH^-(aq) \rightarrow$
   $Fe(OH)_3(s) + 3Na^+(aq) + 3Cl^-(aq)$

   $2K^+(aq) + 2I^-(aq) + Pb^{2+}(aq) + 2NO_3^-(aq) \rightarrow$
   $PbI_2(s) + 2K^+(aq) + 2NO_3^-(aq)$

   $Pb^{2+}(aq) + 2NO_3^-(aq) + 2Na^+(aq) + SO_4^{2-}(aq) \rightarrow$
   $PbSO_4(s) + 2Na^+(aq) + 2NO_3^-(aq)$

   $Ba^{2+}(aq) + 2Cl^-(aq) + 2Na^+(aq) + SO_4^{2-}(aq) \rightarrow$
   $BaSO_4(s) + 2Na^+(aq) + 2Cl^-(aq)$

   $2Na^+(aq) + CO_3^{2-}(aq) + Ba^{2+}(aq) + 2Cl^-(aq) \rightarrow$
   $BaCO_3(s) + 2Na^+(aq) + 2Cl^-(aq)$

   $2Na^+(aq) + CO_3^{2-}(aq) + Cu^{2+}(aq) + SO_4^{2-}(aq) \rightarrow$
   $CuCO_3(s) + 2Na^+(aq) + SO_4^{2-}(aq)$

3. All of the ions are spectator ions, so they all cross out in a net ionic equation. In other words, there is no reaction.

4. Answers may vary. Results should agree with the hypothesis. Disagreements may have resulted from mixtures that contained the wrong solutions, errors in labeling the wells, or failure to observe faint precipitates.

Real-World Chemistry

1. $AgNO_3$ reacts with NaCl in a double-replacement reaction, producing AgCl as a precipitate. The more NaCl the sample contains, the more AgCl will be produced.

2. Complete ionic equation: $Mg^{2+}(aq) + 2OH^-(aq) +$ $2H^+(aq) + 2Cl^-(aq) \rightarrow Mg^{2+}(aq) + 2Cl^-(aq) +$ $2H_2O(l)$. Net ionic equation: $OH^-(aq) + H^+(aq) \rightarrow$ $H_2O(l)$. The product is water.

3. Net ionic equation: $H^+(aq) + HCO_3^-(aq) \rightarrow H_2O(l)$ $+ CO_2(g)$. Using $NaHCO_3$ results in the formation of carbon dioxide gas, which can cause discomfort as it accumulates in the stomach.

Lab 8 ## Determining Avogadro's Number

Use with Section 11.1

Objectives

▶ Measure the diameter of stearic acid solution in a monolayer.
▶ Calculate a value for Avogadro's number.
▶ Infer which volume estimate better approximates the volume of a stearic acid molecule.

Process Skills

Drawing a conclusion, observing and inferring, collecting and interpreting data, measuring and using numbers

Time Allotment

1 class period

Materials

See pages 11T–14T for materials.
(Visit the Chemistry Web site at **science.glencoe.com** *to find links about safety in the laboratory.)*

Safety Precautions

▶ Lycopodium is highly flammable.
▶ Talcum powder can be a respiratory irritant.
▶ Caution students not to breathe the cyclohexane vapors. Use a fume hood.

Alternative Materials

▶ Pentane or hexane could be substituted for cyclohexane as the solvent for stearic acid.
▶ Cetyl alcohol could be used instead of stearic acid.
▶ Space-filling models of stearic acid could be measured for length, width, and depth instead of using the approximations given.

Preparation

Dissolve 0.05 g stearic acid in 500 mL of cyclohexane.

Pre-Lab

1. 6.022×10^{23} particles per mole
2. 7.07×10^{-10} cm^3
3. so that the monolayer is comprised of stearic acid molecules only
4. Answers will vary, but might include that the value for Avogadro's number is more correct when the volume of a single molecule is assumed to be cylindrical.

Teaching the Lab

Have students work in groups of two.

▶ Review the equations for rectangular volume and cylindrical volume.

▶ Caution students to hold the Pasteur pipette perpendicular to the watch glass. The angle at which the pipette is held can be a source of error.

▶ To avoid rounding errors, have students keep 3 significant figures until the final calculations of Avogadro's number.

Hypothesis

The value for Avogadro's number is more correct when the volume of a single molecule is assumed to be cylindrical.

Data and Observations

Data Table 1: Student answers will vary. Values should be between 90 and 120 drops. For calculations, 92 drops is used.

Data Table 2: Answers will vary, depending on the pressure used to squeeze out the drops. An estimate is 70 drops.

Diameter of the watch glass (cm): between 15–20 cm; Assume 20 for calculations.

1. $(91 + 92 + 93)/3 = 92$ drops
2. Mass of stearic acid = 0.10 g/L $\times$ 1 L/1000 mL $\times$ 1 mL/92 drops $\times$ 70 drops = 7.61×10^{-5} g
3. Volume of the monolayer = 7.61×10^{-5} g stearic acid $\times$ 1 cm^3/0.9405 g stearic acid = 8.09×10^{-5} cm^3
4. Thickness of the monolayer (length) = 8.09×10^{-5} cm^3/π(20 cm/2)^2 = 2.58×10^{-7} cm
5. $V_{rec} = 2.58 \times 10^{-7}$ cm $(2.58 \times 10^{-7}$ cm/6$)$ $(2.58 \times 10^{-7}$ cm/6$) = 4.77 \times 10^{-22}$ cm^3/molecule
6. 8.09×10^{-5} cm^3/$(4.77 \times 10^{-22}$ cm^3/molecule$)$ = 1.70×10^{17} molecules
7. 7.61×10^{-5} g stearic acid $\times$ 1 mol stearic acid/284.5 g stearic acid = 2.67×10^{-7} moles stearic acid
8. 1.70×10^{17} molecules stearic acid/2.67×10^{-7} moles stearic acid = 6.3×10^{23} molecules/mole
9. $V_{cyl} = 2.58 \times 10^{-7}$ cm $(\pi((2.58 \times 10^{-7}$ cm/6$)/2)^2)$ = 3.74×10^{-22} cm^3
10. 8.09×10^{-5} cm^3 $\times$ 1 molecule/3.7×10^{-22} cm^3 = 2.16×10^{17} molecules
11. 2.16×10^{17} molecules stearic acid/2.67×10^{-7} moles stearic acid = 8.1×10^{23} molecules/mole

Analyze and Conclude

1. $|6.3 \times 10^{23}$ particles per mole $- 6.02 \times 10^{23}$ particles per mole$|/6.02 \times 10^{23}$ particles per mole $\times 100 = 4.7\%$

   $|8.1 \times 10^{23}$ particles per mole $- 6.02 \times 10^{23}$ particles per mole$|/6.02 \times 10^{23}$ particles per mole $\times 100 = 35\%$

2. The estimate with the lowest percent error; this should be the calculation made from the cylindrical solid.

3. Same as the answer to question 2

Real-World Chemistry

Answers will vary, depending on selected program. All such programs inherently have limitations and assumptions, which will affect the accuracy of the outcomes.

Lab 9 # Measuring Boiling Point

Use with Section 13.4

Objectives

▶ Measure the boiling points of three known liquids.

▶ Correlate boiling point with molar mass and the ability to form hydrogen bonds.

▶ Identify an unknown liquid by its boiling point.

Process Skills

Acquiring and analyzing information, applying concepts, collecting and interpreting data, comparing and contrasting, drawing a conclusion, hypothesizing, making and using tables, measuring and using numbers, observing and inferring, thinking critically

Time Allotment

1 class period

Materials

See pages 11T–14T for materials.

(Visit the Chemistry Web site at **science.glencoe.com** *to find links about safety in the laboratory.)*

Alternative Materials

▶ Isopropyl alcohol (2-propanol) may be used instead of 1-propanol. Do not use both isopropyl alcohol and 1-propanol because it will be more difficult for students to assess the relative importance of molar mass and hydrogen bonding in determining boiling point. Both alcohols have a molar mass of 60. Isopropyl alcohol boils at 82.5°C, and 1-propanol boils at 97.2°C.

► Never, under any circumstances, use gasoline, ether, or other organic liquids that have a low flash point.

Preparation

► Distribute 3 mL samples of the liquids in stoppered test tubes. Do not allow students access to large quantities of the liquids.

► For each group of students, provide a duplicate of one of the sample liquids to be used as the unknown liquid. You may want to give different unknown liquids to different groups.

► Prepare capillary tubes sealed at one end for each sample liquid.

► If another group or class has used the test tubes, make sure they are thoroughly dry.

Pre-Lab

1. Evaporation is vaporization that occurs only at the surface of a liquid. Boiling is vaporization that occurs throughout a liquid.

2. the pressure exerted by a vapor over a liquid

3. Vapor pressure and external pressure are equal when a liquid is at its boiling point.

4. Bubbles of vapor collect below the surface of the liquid and rise to the surface.

5. See Hypothesis.

Teaching the Lab

Have students work in groups of two.

► Many students think that all liquids boil at 100°C. This experiment will demonstrate that each liquid has a characteristic boiling point. Remind students also that a liquid's boiling point depends on the pressure exerted on the liquid. The phase diagrams on page 409 of the textbook illustrate this point.

► Remind students to use a different, clean capillary tube and test tube for each boiling point measurement. One droplet of water at the bottom of a tube can lead to inaccurate results.

► The most common cause of error is failure to notice a steady stream of bubbles from the end of the capillary tube. Tell students to look carefully for the stream of bubbles and to take their temperature reading when the stream stops, not when they first see the stream.

► The chemicals should not be allowed to evaporate to any degree at students' stations or there would be a danger of a flash fire.

Disposal

Place the acetone and alcohols in a shallow pan under the fume hood. Turn the air on in the hood and allow the air flow to evaporate the liquids. Place only a thin layer of liquid in the pan at a time until it is all evaporated. If a fume hood is not available, evaporate the liquid outside.

Hypothesis

Two hypotheses are acceptable: 1-propanol has the highest boiling point and ethanol has the lowest boiling point, or 1-propanol has the highest boiling point and acetone has the lowest boiling point.

Data and Observations

See data table.

Analyze and Conclude

1. See "Molar mass" column in Data Table 1.

2. A steady stream of bubbles indicates that the temperature of the liquid is at the boiling point. The bubbles stop when the temperature decreases to just below the boiling point.

3. The answer will depend on which liquid was used as the unknown. Students should choose the known liquid whose measured boiling point is closest to that of the unknown liquid.

Data and Observations (Lab 9)

Sample Data

Data Table 1				
Liquid	**Molar formula**	**Molar mass (g)**	**Hydrogen bonding?**	**Boiling point (°C)**
Acetone	C_3H_6O	58	no	55.9
Ethanol	C_2H_5O	45	yes	79.2
1-propanol	C_3H_8O	60	yes	96.5
Unknown	—	—	—	81.3

4. Hydrogen bonding seems to be more important. Ethanol has a lower molar mass than does acetone. Thus, based on molar mass, ethanol should have the lower boiling point. Ethanol forms hydrogen bonds, but acetone does not. Thus, based on hydrogen bonding, ethanol should have a higher boiling point. Based on ethanol's higher boiling point, hydrogen bonds have a greater effect than molar mass.

5. acetone, 56.5°C; ethanol, 78.5°C; 1-propanol, 97.2°C

6. Answers may vary. Percentage errors for the sample data are 1.1% for acetone, 0.9 for ethanol, and 0.7% for 1-propanol. Students may have made inaccurate temperature measurements. The atmospheric pressure in the laboratory may have been higher or lower than standard atmospheric pressure.

Real-World Chemistry

1. It would take longer to cook noodles in boiling water at an altitude of 3000 m. Atmospheric pressure decreases with altitude, and the phase diagram for water shows that boiling point decreases as pressure decreases. Therefore, water boils at a lower temperature at high altitude than at sea level. Because noodles cooked at 3000 m elevation will be cooking in water that is cooler than boiling water at sea level, they will take longer to cook.

2. Because the molar masses of the molecules in cooking oil are comparatively high, the boiling points of these molecules are much higher than the boiling point of water. Because oil can be heated to a much higher temperature than can water, foods fried in oil cook more rapidly than they do when boiled in water.

3. The boiling point of 1,2-ethanediol is much higher than that of water, so a water–antifreeze mixture can absorb much more heat from an engine without boiling over than water alone can absorb.

Lab 10 Relating Gas Pressure and Gas Volume

Use with Section 14.1

Objectives

▶ Measure the volume of the air sample at different pressures.

▶ Make and use a graph of volume versus pressure to illustrate the mathematical relationship.

Process Skills

Applying concepts, collecting and interpreting data, drawing a conclusion, hypothesizing, making and using graphs, making and using tables, measuring and using numbers

Time Allotment

1 class period

Materials

See pages 11T–14T for materials.

(Visit the Chemistry Web site at **science.glencoe.com** *to find links about safety in the laboratory.)*

Alternative Materials

▶ A sealed plastic syringe could be used instead of a Boyle's law apparatus. The syringe should be supported so that it does not fall over when objects are placed on the plunger.

▶ The objects to be placed on the plunger could be books, blocks of wood, or any other fairly dense items that are flat and stackable.

Preparation

▶ Provide a collection of stackable objects that have masses of approximately 500–550 g.

▶ If you are using a plastic syringe, attach the cap to the tip of the syringe and seal around the cap with epoxy cement, silicone sealant, or melted paraffin.

Pre-Lab

1. The volume of a given amount of gas held at a constant temperature varies inversely with the pressure.

2. Pressure is force per unit area.

3. Pressure = $12.7 \text{ N}/(3.14 \times (6.20 \times 10^{-2} \text{ m})^2)$ = 1050 N/m^2.

4. The variable y decreases as x increases.

5. See Hypothesis.

Teaching the Lab

Have students work in groups of two.

▶ One student may have to support the objects on the apparatus or syringe while the other student makes the volume measurements. Have students switch roles in different trials.

▶ Caution students not to press down or lift up as they support the objects. Ask students to explain why doing so could affect their measurements. (Pressing down would increase the force on the plunger, and lifting up would decrease it.)

Copyright © Glencoe/McGraw-Hill, a division of the McGraw-Hill Companies, Inc.

▶ Before students make their graphs, ask them whether they expect the data points to fall along a straight line. (no) Ask them what kind of curve is predicted by Boyle's law. (a downward curve)

Hypothesis

The volume of the air sample will decrease as the pressure increases.

Data and Observations

See data table.
1. See "Area of plunger head" cell in data table.
2. See "Total Mass" column in data table.
3. See "Force" column in data table.
4. See "Pressure" column in data table.
5. See "Total Pressure" column in data table.
6. See "Average" column in data table.

Analyze and Conclude

1. Students' graphs should look similar to the following:

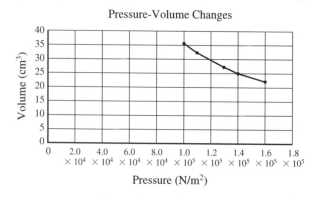

Pressure-Volume Changes

2. Answers may vary. Results should show that average volume decreased as total pressure increased.
3. Yes, the results would have been different. Boyle's law applies only when the temperature remains constant. If the temperature changes, the volume also changes.
4. Answers may vary. Results should agree with the hypothesis. Disagreements may have resulted from leakage of air past the head of the plunger, excessive friction between the head and the barrel, or errors in measuring masses or volumes or in performing the calculations.

Real-World Chemistry

1. $P_1V_1 = P_2V_2$. Rearranging gives $P_2 = (V_1/V_2)P_1$. $P_1 = 1.0 \times 10^5$ N/m^2, and $V_1 = 8V_2$. Substituting gives $P_2 = (8V_2/V_2)(1.0 \times 10^5$ N/m$^2)$ $= 8.0 \times 10^5$ N/m^2.
2. $P_1V_1 = P_2V_2$. Rearranging gives $V_2 = (P_1/P_2)V_1$ $= ((1.0 \times 10^5$ N/m$^2)/(2.3 \times 10^4$ N/m$^2)) \times 200.0$ L $= 870$ L.
3. The pressure in the bubbles decreases and the volume increases as the diver ascends. If the diver ascends too quickly, the bubbles may become large enough to block blood vessels before the gas can be removed from the body.

Data and Observations (Lab 10)

Sample Data

Data Table 1								
Mass of object 1 (g): 523				Mass of object 3 (g): 555				
Mass of object 2 (g): 568				Mass of object 4 (g): 518				
Diameter of plunger head (mm): 22				Area of plunger head (m^2): 3.8×10^{-4}				
Stacked Objects	Total Mass (kg)	Force (N)	Pressure (N/m^2)	Total Pressure (N/m^2)	Volume (cm^3)			
					Trial 1	Trial 2	Trial 3	Average
none	0	0	0	1.0×10^5	35.4	35.4	35.4	35.4
1	0.523	5.13	1.4×10^4	1.1×10^5	32.1	31.7	32.8	32.2
1, 2	1.091	10.7	2.8×10^4	1.3×10^5	27.0	27.7	26.9	27.2
1, 2, 3	1.646	16.1	4.2×10^4	1.4×10^5	25.2	25.4	25.3	25.3
1, 2, 3, 4	2.164	21.2	5.6×10^4	1.6×10^5	22.9	21.7	21.7	22.1

Lab 11 Effect of Temperature on Solubility

Use with Section 15.1

Objectives

▶ Collect ammonia gas from a concentrated ammonia solution.

▶ Measure the time required for ammonia gas to dissolve in water at four different temperatures.

▶ Relate the time it takes the ammonia to dissolve to solubility.

Process Skills

Applying concepts, collecting and interpreting data, comparing and contrasting, hypothesizing, making and using graphs, making and using tables, measuring and using numbers, observing and inferring, thinking critically

Time Allotment

1 class period

Materials

See pages 11T–14T for materials.

*(Visit the Chemistry Web site at **science.glencoe.com** to find links about safety in the laboratory.)*

Alternative Materials

▶ A hot plate, Bunsen burner, or microwave oven may be used to heat water to temperatures higher than that of hot tap water.

▶ A clock with a second hand may be used instead of a stopwatch.

Preparation

▶ Make sure the fume hood is working properly before preparing the concentrated ammonia solution and before students begin the experiment.

▶ Make enough concentrated ammonia solution to provide about 5 mL to each group of students. Keep the solution under the fume hood.

Pre-Lab

1. Solubility is a measure of the maximum amount of a solute that will dissolve in a given amount of solvent at a specified temperature and pressure.

2. Decreasing the temperature decreases the solubility of most solids.

3. Decreasing the temperature increases the solubility of gases in liquid solvents.

4. The solubility would double. Solubility is directly proportional to pressure (Henry's law).

5. Decreasing the temperature will decrease the time required for the ammonia to dissolve in water. Gases are more soluble in liquids at lower temperatures, and the more soluble a solute is, the more rapidly it will dissolve.

Teaching the Lab

Have students work in groups of two.

▶ Have students in each group split their activities when possible. For example, one student can fill beakers with water and measure temperature while the other is collecting ammonia gas in the collecting pipette.

▶ Warn students to keep the tip of the collecting pipette pointing downward when moving it from the generating pipette to the beaker of water in step 8.

▶ Make sure students understand that they are not directly measuring the solubility of ammonia. Rather, they are measuring the time required for ammonia to dissolve. Explain that solubility can be inferred from the time because a solute that is more soluble takes less time to dissolve.

Disposal

Completely empty the ammonia gas under the fume hood. Wash the containers and flush the wash water down the drain.

Data and Observations (Lab 11)

Data Table 1			
	Temperature (°C)	**Temperature (K)**	**Time (s)**
Hot water	50.3	323.3	65
Hot water + cold water	36.1	309.1	42
Cold water	21.6	294.6	30
Cold water + ice	0.2	273.2	18

Hypothesis

Decreasing the temperature will decrease the time required for ammonia to dissolve in water.

Data and Observations

See data table.

Analyze and Conclude

1. The molecular weights of NH_3, N_2, and O_2 are 17, 28, and 32, respectively. Therefore, NH_3 is the least dense of the three gases, and it will rise to the top of the collecting pipette, forcing the other gases out the bottom.

2. As ammonia gas dissolves in the water, the pressure inside the collecting pipette decreases, thereby drawing water into the pipette.

3. Student graphs should look similar to the graph shown here.

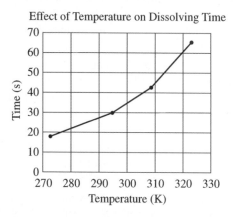

Effect of Temperature on Dissolving Time

4. Results suggest that solubility increases as temperature decreases. This conclusion agrees with the data in Table 15-2.

5. Answers may vary. Dissolving time should decrease with temperature. Disagreements may result from waiting too long to place the collecting pipette in the water after measuring the water's temperature.

Real-World Chemistry

1. Because the solubility of CO_2 in water decreases with temperature, less CO_2 could be dissolved in ocean water at higher temperatures. This would cause the level of CO_2 in the atmosphere to rise.

2. Stagnant pools can have a low O_2 content due to the limited mixing of air and water. Gulping air allows the fish to get more O_2. Less O_2 can dissolve in warm water than in cold water, so the fish in warm water must gulp air more frequently to get enough O_2.

3. Yes; the beverage has a lower CO_2 solubility at higher temperatures. Therefore, when the warmer bottle is opened, there is a more rapid escape of CO_2 from solution, which is more likely to cause the beverage to bubble over.

Lab 12 Specific Heat of Metals
Use with Section 16.2

Objectives

▶ Construct a calorimeter.

▶ Measure changes in the temperature of water in the calorimeter when warmer metals are added.

▶ Calculate the specific heat of each metal.

Process Skills

Applying concepts, collecting and interpreting data, comparing and contrasting, drawing a conclusion, hypothesizing, measuring and using numbers, observing and inferring

Time Allotment

1 class period

Materials

See pages 11T–14T for materials.
(Visit the Chemistry Web site at science.glencoe.com to find links about safety in the laboratory.)

Safety Precautions

▶ Use non-mercury thermometers.

▶ Use GFCI protection in electrical sources.

Alternative Materials

▶ Depending upon availability, other metals could be used. Copper wire can be stripped of its insulation, and sinkers made of tin may be purchased from fishing tackle stores.

▶ A thermistor probe attached to an electronic thermometer could be used instead of a glass thermometer.

Preparation

▶ Metal samples must be small enough to be completely submerged in the water in the calorimeter.

▶ Place different metal samples in separate labeled boxes.

Pre-Lab

1. the amount of heat required to raise the temperature of one gram of a substance by one degree Celsius

2. Specific heat $= c = q/(m \times \Delta T) = 795$ J/$(123$ g $\times (45.1 - 17.6)°C) = 0.235$ J/$(g \cdot °C)$.

3. an insulated device used for measuring the amount of heat absorbed or released during a chemical or physical process

4. The insulating material keeps most of the heat that is transferred during the process from leaving the system.

5. Aluminum will cause the largest change in water temperature for its mass. Aluminum has the highest specific heat of the three metals, so it can release the most heat per gram to the water in the calorimeter.

Teaching the Lab

Have students work in groups of two.

▶ Remind students to check the water level in the beaker on the hot plate as the water boils. Point out that the level will drop each time a test tube is removed. Tell them to add more water to the beaker if the level starts to drop below the tops of the metal samples.

▶ Ask students why it is reasonable to assume that, after 10 min in boiling water, the metal samples are at the same temperature as the water. (As the water gets hotter, it supplies heat to the samples. Once it starts to boil, its temperature stays the same, and it continues to heat the samples until they reach the same temperature.)

▶ Emphasize the importance of speed in transferring the metals from the boiling water to the calorimeter and in covering the calorimeter. Caution students not to allow

any hot water to drip from the outside of the test tube into the calorimeter during the transfer.

Hypothesis

Aluminum will cause the largest change in water temperature for its mass.

Data and Observations

See data table.

1. See "Change in water temperature" row in data table.
2. See "Change in metal temperature" row in data table.
3. See "Heat gained by water" row in data table.
4. See "Specific heat" row in data table.

Analyze and Conclude

1. Factors include the rate at which heat moves from the system (water and metal) to the surroundings (cups and air) as well as the specific heat of the surroundings. If too much heat leaves the system, the assumption is not valid.

2. Answers may vary. Results should be close to 0.2°C/g for aluminum, 0.1°C/g for iron, and 0.03°C/g for lead. These results support the hypothesis that aluminum will cause the largest change in water temperature for its mass.

3. Aluminum has the highest specific heat, measured in J/$(g \cdot °C)$, so it releases the most heat (J) for a given decrease in temperature (°C) and a given mass (g).

4. Answers may vary. Sources of error may include loss of heat from the calorimeter to the surroundings, inaccuracy in measuring masses, volumes, or temperatures, or rounding to two significant figures in the calculations.

Data and Observations (Lab 12)

Data Table 1			
	Aluminum	**Iron**	**Lead**
Mass of metal (g)	48.3	63.5	90.4
Volume of water (mL)	72.7	77.3	75.6
Initial water temperature (°C)	20.6	20.5	20.6
Initial metal temperature (°C)	100.0	100.0	100.0
Final temperature (°C)	30.5	26.9	23.4
Change in water temperature (°C)	9.9	6.4	2.8
Change in metal temperature (°C)	69.5	73.1	76.6
Heat gained by water (J)	3000	2100	890
Specific heat, J/$(g \cdot °C)$	0.89	0.45	0.13

Real-World Chemistry

1. The sinker would reach the lake-water temperature more quickly if it was made of lead. Lead has a lower specific heat, so it must release less heat per gram to experience a given decrease in temperature.

2. Both the foil and the pan are made of aluminum, so they have the same specific heat. However, the foil has a small mass, so it contains only a small amount of heat that can be transferred to your hands. That amount is not enough to cause burns. The pan has a much larger mass and can transfer enough heat to burn your hands.

3. No, this information would not be enough to identify the metal because both lead and gold have a specific heat of 0.129 J/(g·°C). One way to identify the metal without equipment would be to compare its appearance with that of lead and gold.

Lab 13 Energy Changes in Chemical and Physical Processes

Use with Section 16.5

Objectives

▶ Measure the temperature of four systems before and after a chemical or physical process.
▶ Calculate the change in temperature of each system during the process.
▶ Observe physical changes that occur during each process.
▶ Deduce whether each process is spontaneous.

Process Skills

Applying concepts, classifying, collecting and interpreting data, drawing a conclusion, making and using tables, measuring and using numbers, observing and inferring, thinking critically

Time Allotment

1 class period

Materials

See pages 11T–14T for materials.
Visit the Chemistry Web site at **science.glencoe.com** *to find links about safety in the laboratory.*

Alternative Materials

▶ Any solid chemical that is soluble in water may be used instead of NH_4Cl or $NaHCO_3$ in wells A1 or A2.
▶ Reactions may be carried out in small test tubes instead of on a microplate.

Preparation

Allow the NH_4Cl, $NaHCO_3$, water, and HCl to come to room temperature before students begin the experiment.

Pre-Lab

1. In exothermic processes, energy is released; in endothermic processes, energy is absorbed.
2. ΔH_{system} is negative in an exothermic process and positive in an endothermic process.
3. The entropy of the system usually increases.
4. $\Delta G_{system} = \Delta H_{system} - T\Delta S_{system}$
5. A process is spontaneous when ΔG_{system} is negative.

Teaching the Lab

Have students work in groups of two.

▶ Caution students that HCl is corrosive and will irritate the eyes, skin, and respiratory tract. Instruct them to clean up all spills immediately.
▶ Have students begin measuring the temperature of the solution in each well as soon as they finish mixing the contents of the well. They are to record the lowest temperature attained by solutions that become cooler after mixing and the highest temperature attained by solutions that become warmer after mixing.
▶ If students think they may have made a mistake with a mixture, have them repeat the mixture in another well.
▶ Use non-mercury based thermometers.
▶ Remind students to never place a pipette in their mouth.

Data and Observations

See data table.

Analyze and Conclude

1. Any chemicals that are not initially at room temperature will either gain heat from the room or lose heat to the room until they reach room temperature.
2. well A1, endothermic; well A2, exothermic; well B1, endothermic; well B2, endothermic
3. well A1, positive; well A2, negative; well B1, positive; well B2, positive
4. positive for all reactions

Data and Observations (Lab 13)

		Temperature (°C)			
Well	Contents	Before mixing	After mixing	Temperature change (°C)	Observations
A1	$NH_4Cl + H_2O$	23°C	17°C	−6°C	solid dissolves
A2	$NaHCO_3 + H_2O$	23°C	26°C	+3°C	solid dissolves
B1	$NH_4Cl + HCl$	23°C	18°C	−5°C	solid dissolves
B2	$NaHCO_3 + HCl$	23°C	18°C	−5°C	solid dissolves; bubbles form

Data Table 1

5. The process in well A2 will always occur spontaneously; the other reactions will occur spontaneously only at higher temperatures.

Real-World Chemistry

1. The conversion of graphite to diamond is never spontaneous. $\Delta H_{system} = +1.90$ kJ. $\Delta S_{system} = S_{products} - S_{reactants} = 2.4$ J/K − 5.7 J/K = −3.3 J/K. A process in which ΔH_{system} is positive and ΔS_{system} is negative is never spontaneous.

2. Yes, the combustion is spontaneous at 25°C. $\Delta G_{system} = \Delta H_{system} - T\Delta S_{system} = -6535$ kJ − [298 K × (−0.4391 kJ/K)] = −6404 kJ. Because ΔG_{system} is negative, the reaction is spontaneous.

3. $\Delta G_{system} = \Delta H_{system} - T\Delta S_{system}$. Rearranging gives $T = -(\Delta G_{system} - \Delta H_{system})/\Delta S_{system}$. Substituting gives −(0.1 kJ − 176 kJ)/0.285 kJ/K = 618 K, or 345°C.

Lab 14 Determining Reaction Orders

Use with Section 17.3

Objectives

- Measure the time needed for reactions to occur.
- Compare rates of chemical reactions.
- Infer general rate equation from experimental data.
- Determine a value for the order of reaction from experimental data.

Process Skills

Observing and inferring, acquiring and analyzing information, collecting and interpreting data, measuring and using numbers, hypothesizing, thinking critically

Time Allotment

1 class period

Materials

See pages 11T–14T for materials.

(Visit the Chemistry Web site at science.glencoe.com to find links about safety in the laboratory.)

Alternative Materials

- 10-mL beakers or small test tubes and test-tube rack can be substituted for the 24-well microplate.
- If Pasteur pipettes are used instead of droppers, the number of drops listed in the data table must be doubled or tripled depending on how many drops equal 1 mL. Caution students to never place a pipette in their mouth.

Preparation

- To make $2.0 \times 10^{-4}M$ crystal violet solution, dissolve 0.082 g of crystal violet powder in enough water to equal 1 L of solution. Each group of two students needs 2 mL solution.
- To make 1.0M NaOH solution, dissolve 4.0 g of NaOH pellets in enough water to equal 1 L of solution. Each group of two students needs 5 mL of solution.

Pre-Lab

1. The value of m must be greater than zero, probably 1 or 2.
2. The color disappears.

3. to more easily recognize the color change

4. Sodium hydroxide is present in excess. You do not know how much of it is left, so you cannot complete the calculations.

5. Refer to Hypothesis.

Teaching the Lab

Have students work in groups of two.

▶ Review with students the definition of rate and its dependence on concentration.

▶ Review the equations for calculating order of reaction and for determining reactant concentration.

▶ Explain that the color change is due to the bonding of an OH^- ion with the acidic form of the crystal violet molecule. Help students understand why the concentration of CV^+ is zero at the end of the reaction.

▶ You may want to point out to students that crystal violet can be used as a visual indicator in some acid–base reactions.

Hypothesis

Answers will vary depending on which value (0, 1, or 2) students choose for the values of m and n. One possible combination is $m = 1$; $n = 1$.

Data and Observations

See data tables.

1. For reactions 1 and 2: $2 \times 10^{-4}M \times 5$ drops/30 drops solution = $3.3 \times 10^{-5}M$. For reaction 3: $2 \times 10^{-4}M \times 3$ drops/30 drops solution = $2.0 \times 10^{-5}M$.

2. For reactions 1 and 3: $0.1M \times 20$ drops/30 drops solution = $6.7 \times 10^{-2}M$. For reaction 2: $0.1M \times 10$ drops/30 drops solution = $3.3 \times 10^{-2}M$.

3. For reaction 1: $3.3 \times 10^{-5}M/360$ s = $9.2 \times 10^{-8}M$.
For reaction 2: $3.3 \times 10^{-5}M/720$ s = $4.6 \times 10^{-8}M$.
For reaction 3: $2.0 \times 10^{-5}M/420$ s = $4.8 \times 10^{-8}M$.

4. $\log\left[\dfrac{9.2 \times 10^{-8}M}{4.8 \times 10^{-8}M}\right] = n \log\left[\dfrac{3.3 \times 10^{-5}M}{2.0 \times 10^{-5}M}\right]$;
$n = 1.3$

5. $\log\left[\dfrac{9.2 \times 10^{-8}M}{4.6 \times 10^{-8}M}\right] = m \log\left[\dfrac{6.7 \times 10^{-2}M}{3.3 \times 10^{-2}M}\right]$;
$m = 9.8$

6. Rate = $k[CV^+]^{1.3}[NaOH]^{0.98}$ or
Rate = $k[CV^+]^1[NaOH]^1$

Analyze and Conclude

1. The iodine does not participate in the rate-liming step. It does not affect the rate.

2. Answers will vary. Examples of error are: droppers were not calibrated, multiple runs were not performed, sample size may be too small, and estimating the position of the second hand or time needed to stop the stopwatch.

3. Answers may vary, but calculations should be done correctly.

Percent error = $\dfrac{\text{your value} - \text{literature value}}{\text{literature value}} \times 100\%$

Real-World Chemistry

a. Rate = $k[\text{ethyl acetate}]^1$ or Rate = $k[\text{ethyl acetate}]^1[\text{H2O}]^0$

b. Rate = $k[\text{ethyl acetate}]^1[\text{HCl}]^1$

Data and Observations (Lab 14)

Sample Data

Data Table 1				
Reaction mixture	Crystal violet (drops)	0.1M NaOH (drops)	Distilled water (drops)	Time (s)
1	5	20	5	360
2	5	10	15	720
3	3	20	7	420

Data Table 2			
Reaction mixture	Crystal violet (M)	NaOH (M)	Rate (M/s)
1	3.3×10^{-5}	6.7×10^{-2}	9.2×10^{-8}
2	3.3×10^{-5}	3.3×10^{-2}	4.6×10^{-8}
3	2.0×10^{-5}	6.7×10^{-2}	4.8×10^{-8}

Lab 15 Observing Equilibrium

Use with Section 18.1

Objectives
▶ Observe color changes associated with shifts in equilibrium.
▶ Relate changes in reactant concentration to the direction of shift in equilibrium.

Process Skills
Observing and inferring, hypothesizing, predicting, making and using tables, comparing and contrasting

Time Allotment
1 class period

Materials
See pages 11T–14T for materials.
*(Visit the Chemistry Web site at **science.glencoe.com** to find links about safety in the laboratory.)*

Alternative Materials
Any equilibrium system may be used as long as reactants and products have different colors. Ions used to form precipitates or complex ions will need to be chosen according to the chemistry of the system selected. For any alternative materials, be sure to use personal protective equipment such as safety goggles, gloves, and an apron.

Preparation
▶ To make 0.1M KSCN solution, dissolve 9.7 g KSCN in enough distilled water to make 1.00 L of solution. Make the solution on the day of the experiment.
▶ To make 0.1M $Fe(NO_3)_3$ solution, dissolve 40.40 g $Fe(NO_3)_3 \cdot 9H_2O$ in enough distilled water to make 1.00 L of solution. Make the solution on the day of the experiment.
▶ To make 1.0M NaOH solution, dissolve 40.0 g NaOH in enough distilled water to make 1.00 L of solution.
▶ To make 0.1M $AgNO_3$ solution, dissolve 17.0 g $AgNO_3$ in enough distilled water to make 1.00 L of solution.
▶ Each group of students requires 4.0 mL $Fe(NO_3)_3$ solution, 4.0 mL KSCN solution, 2 mL NaOH solution, 0.4 mL $AgNO_3$ solution, 0.5 g $Fe(NO_3)_3$, 0.5 g NH_4SCN, and 0.5 g KCl.

Pre-Lab
1. decrease
2. purplish
3. Cl^- ion
4. toward the products (right)
5. See Hypothesis.

Teaching the Lab
Have students work in groups of two.
▶ Review with students the definition of equilibrium. Make sure students understand the mass action expression is equal to a constant and how the expression relates to shifts when reactant concentration is increased or decreased.
▶ Discuss the chemical equation with students in terms of the colors they may see. Students should realize that although the reactants are both colorless solutions, a shift in color from red to light orange or yellow is a shift toward reactants. They should also recognize that such a shift means that the disturbance either increased the concentration of $FeSCN^{2+}$ or decreased the concentration of one of the two reactants.
▶ Caution students not to put the reaction mixtures or any excess reagents down the drain.

Hypothesis
Answers will vary depending on which effect students choose. The K^+ ion is a spectator ion, but the Cl^- ion competes with the SCN^- ion to form a complex ion with the iron(III) ion. One possible hypothesis statement is: the color will become less red because $FeSCN^{2+}$ ions will decompose.

Data and Observations
See data tables.

Analyze and Conclude
1. reactant
2. decrease
3. The color of the solution became light orange (or yellowish). This means that the red $FeSCN^{2+}$ ions were decomposing to make more reactant particles. Therefore, the $AgNO_3$ was removing SCN^- ions.
4. (a) When reactant ions are removed, the equilibrium shifts left. (b) When reactant ions are added, the equilibrium shifts right.

Data and Observations (Lab 15)

Sample Data

Data Table 1	
Substance	**Color**
$Fe(NO_3)_3$	colorless
KSCN	colorless
$FeSCN^{2+}$ ion	dark red

Data Table 2							
Test-tube number	**Substance disturbing equilibrium**	**Common ion added**	**Color after stirring**	**Color is most like**		**Equilibrium shifts toward**	
				Reactants	**Products**	**Left**	**Right**
1	0.5 g $Fe(NO_3)_3$	Fe^{3+}	darker red		✓		✓
2	0.5 g NH_4SCN	SCN^-	darker red		✓		✓
3	0.5 g KCl	none	lighter red or orange	✓		✓	
4	1.0M NaOH	none	colorless solution; white precipitate (may have yellowish tint)	✓		✓	
5	0.1M $AgNO_3$	none	colorless solution; white precipitate	✓		✓	

Real-World Chemistry

1. Answers will vary but should mention that the formation of NH_3 is maximized by the use of a catalyst, by control of temperature, and by drawing off some of the NH_3 as it was formed.

2. As the carbon dioxide escapes, the equilibrium shifts to the left.

Lab 16 Exploring Chemical Equilibrium

Use with Section 18.2

Objectives

▶ Prepare serial dilutions of a standard solution.

▶ Estimate the color intensity of solutions at equilibrium.

▶ Relate color-intensity values to the concentration of $FeSCN^{2+}$ at equilibrium.

▶ Calculate the equilibrium constant for the reaction between Fe^{3+} and SCN^-.

Process Skills

Applying concepts, collecting and interpreting data, drawing a conclusion, hypothesizing, measuring and using numbers, observing and inferring

Time Allotment

1 class period

Materials

See pages 11T–14T for materials.

(Visit the Chemistry Web site at **science.glencoe.com** *to find links about safety in the laboratory.)*

Safety Precautions

KSCN emits toxic fumes of cyanide when in contact with concentrated acids.

Alternative Materials

▶ Reactions could be carried out in test tubes instead of microplate wells. Larger volumes of solutions would have to be used.

▶ Instead of estimating the intensity of the red color, students could use a spectrophotometer to measure the absorbance of each reaction mixture at a wavelength of 590 nm.

Preparation

▶ Prepare enough of each standard solution so that students can repeat a mixture if they make a mistake.

▶ To reduce the number of pipettes required, provide a labeled pipette with each standard solution. Warn students not to contaminate pipettes with other solutions.

Pre-Lab

1. In a homogenous equilibrium, all reactants and products are in the same physical state. In a heterogeneous equilibrium, the reactants and products are in more than one physical state. The reaction between Fe^{3+} and SCN^- is a homogenous equilibrium.

2. $K_{eq} = [FeSCN^{2+}]/[Fe^{3+}][SCN^-]$

3. It would decrease the concentration of $FeSCN^{2+}$. According to Le Châtelier's principle, decreasing the concentration of a reactant shifts the equilibrium to the left.

4. It would have no effect on the equilibrium constant, which is always the same for a given reaction at a given temperature.

5. The color intensity will decrease from well A1 to well A6. Well A1 has the highest $[Fe^{3+}]$, and well A6 has the lowest. $[FeSCN^{2+}]$ varies with $[Fe^{3+}]$, and the color intensity varies with $[FeSCN^{2+}]$.

Teaching the Lab

Have students work in groups of two.

▶ Caution students not to contaminate wells by using pipettes that have contacted the solutions in other wells.

▶ Emphasize that well D6 is used only to prepare the dilutions of $Fe(NO_3)_3$ solution. Students should not attempt to estimate the color intensity of the mixture that is left in this well.

▶ Discuss with students the rationale for assuming that all of the SCN^- was consumed in the reaction in well A1. Explain that because the $[Fe^{3+}]$ after mixing (1.00×10^{-1} M) was 100 times larger than the $[SCN^-]$ after mixing (1.00×10^{-3} M), *almost* all of the SCN^- was consumed. Explain that the error caused by this assumption should be small compared with other uncertainties in the experiment.

▶ Be sure students understand the purpose of estimating the color intensity for each well. Explain that the color intensity is proportional to the $[FeSCN^{2+}]$ at equilibrium. Therefore, if they know the $[FeSCN^{2+}]$ for one of the wells (A1), they can infer the $[FeSCN^{2+}]$ for the other wells.

Hypothesis

The color intensity will decrease from well A1 to well A6.

Data and Observations

See data table for sample data.

1. See "$[Fe^{3+}]$ after mixing" column in data table.
2. See "$[SCN^-]$ after mixing" column in data table.
3. See first-row entries in "$[FeSCN^{2+}]$ at equilibrium," "$[SCN^-]$ at equilibrium," and "$[Fe^{3+}]$ at equilibrium," columns in data table.
4. See "$[FeSCN^{2+}]$ at equilibrium" column in data table.
5. See "$[SCN^-]$ at equilibrium" column in data table.
6. See "$[Fe^{3+}]$ at equilibrium" column in data table.
7. See "K_{eq}" column in data table.

Data and Observations (Lab 16)   Sample Data

Data Table 1								
Well	$[Fe^{3+}]$ before mixing (*M*)	$[Fe^{3+}]$ after mixing (*M*)	$[SCN^-]$ after mixing (*M*)	Color intensity*	$[FeSCN^{2+}]$ at equilibrium (*M*)	$[SCN^-]$ at equilibrium (*M*)	$[Fe^{3+}]$ at equilibrium (*M*)	K_{eq}
A1	0.200	1.00×10^{-1}	1.00×10^{-3}	1.00	1.00×10^{-3}	0	9.9×10^{-2}	—
A2	0.100	5.00×10^{-2}	1.00×10^{-3}	0.44	4.4×10^{-4}	5.6×10^{-4}	5.0×10^{-2}	16
A3	0.0500	2.50×10^{-2}	1.00×10^{-3}	0.24	2.4×10^{-4}	7.6×10^{-4}	2.5×10^{-2}	13
A4	0.0250	1.25×10^{-2}	1.00×10^{-3}	0.12	1.2×10^{-4}	8.8×10^{-4}	1.2×10^{-2}	11
A5	0.0125	6.25×10^{-3}	1.00×10^{-3}	0.05	5.1×10^{-5}	9.5×10^{-4}	6.2×10^{-3}	8.7
A6	0.00625	3.13×10^{-3}	1.00×10^{-3}	0.03	3.1×10^{-5}	9.7×10^{-4}	3.1×10^{-3}	10

* Values were derived using a spectrophotometer.

Analyze and Conclude

1. Answers may vary. Color intensity values should decrease from well A1 through well A6, supporting the hypothesis. However, differences at the high and low ends of the color-intensity range may be difficult to resolve.

2. The equilibrium constant and the relative concentrations of reactants and products would be different. The equilibrium would be shifted to the left if the reaction is exothermic and to the right if the reaction is endothermic.

3. Answers may vary. Students should recognize that all of the calculated values for K_{eq} should theoretically be identical and that greater variation among values means less precision.

4. Answers may vary. Sources of imprecision may include the assumption that all of the SCN^- was consumed in the reaction in well A1, errors in measuring volumes, and inaccuracy in estimating color intensity.

Real-World Chemistry

1. Answers may vary. The kit would contain a specific volume of KSCN solution at a specific concentration. Users of the kit would be instructed to mix a specific volume of room-temperature water with the KSCN solution. They would then compare the color of the mixture with a chart that relates the color to the approximate level of Fe^{3+} in the water.

2. According to Le Châtelier's principle, removing ethyl acetate would shift the equilibrium to the right, increasing the production of ethyl acetate. Removing water or adding more acetic acid or ethanol should have the same effect.

Lab 17 Comparing the Strengths of Acids

Use with Section 19.3

Objectives

▶ Prepare serial dilutions of standard acid solutions.
▶ Measure the pH of the standard and diluted solutions.
▶ Calculate the H^+ ion concentration of each solution and the K_a of each weak acid.
▶ Rank the acids in order of strength.

Process Skills

Acquiring and analyzing information, applying concepts, comparing and contrasting, drawing a conclusion, making and using tables, measuring and using numbers

Time Allotment

1 class period

Materials

See pages 11T–14T for materials.

*(Visit the Chemistry Web site at **science.glencoe.com** to find links about safety in the laboratory.)*

Alternative Materials

▶ Other strong or weak acids could be used instead of or in addition to those listed.
▶ A pH meter could be used instead of pH paper.
▶ Solutions could be made up in test tubes instead of microplate wells, and volumes could be measured with a graduated cylinder instead of by counting drops from a thin-stem pipette.

Preparation

▶ Prepare enough of each standard acid solution so that students can repeat parts of the procedure if they make a mistake.
▶ To reduce the number of pipettes required, provide a labeled pipette with each acid solution. Warn students not to contaminate pipettes with other solutions.

Pre-Lab

1. A weak acid is an acid that ionizes only partially in dilute aqueous solution. A dilute acid is a solution that contains a low concentration of acid molecules.
2. Formic acid is stronger because its K_a is larger.
3. The pH of a solution is the negative logarithm of the hydrogen ion concentration.
4. See Hypothesis.
5. $K_a = [H^+][A^-]/[HA]$

Teaching the Lab

Have students work in groups of two.

▶ Caution students not to contaminate solutions by using pipettes that have contacted the solutions in other rows of the microplate.
▶ Remind students that they should measure the pH of the solutions in microplate columns 1 and 3 but not 2. Explain that the concentration difference between columns 1 and 2 or between columns 2 and 3 is not great enough to produce a large difference in pH.
▶ If students have difficulty with the calculations in this experiment, refer them to Example Problem 19-5 in the textbook, which works through the same calculations step by step.

Hypothesis

Decreasing the concentration of a weak acid would shift the equilibrium to the left, decreasing the concentration of H^+ ions and thus increasing the pH of the solution. There would be no effect on the K_a of the acid because that is a constant for a given temperature.

Data and Observations

1–5. See data table for sample data.

Analyze and Conclude

1. An acid concentration of zero means that the acid has completely ionized, which is the definition of a strong acid.

2. Permanganic acid is the strongest acid (a strong acid). It is followed in order by citric acid, boric acid, and hydrogen peroxide (all weak acids).

3. Boric acid, 5.4×10^{-10} at 293 K; citric acid, 7.2×10^{-4} at 293 K; hydrogen peroxide, 2.4×10^{-12} at 298 K. Percent error in the sample data: boric acid, 50%; citric acid, 18%; hydrogen peroxide, 38%. The largest source of error probably involves the limited precision of pH paper and mistakes in determining pH on the basis of the color of the paper. Other sources may include inaccuracy in performing dilutions or rounding to two significant figures in the calculations.

Real-World Chemistry

1. Amino acids have K_a values ranging from 1.5×10^{-2} to 1.5×10^{-3}. The K_a of DNA is approximately 1×10^{-1}. Amino acids and DNA are weaker than permanganic acid but stronger than citric acid, boric acid, and hydrogen peroxide.

2. No, it would not be a good idea. Lemons and oranges are citrus fruits, which contain citric acid and other acids. Compost made from the rinds of citrus fruits could make the soil acidic, causing the plant to produce blue flowers.

3. Sulfur oxides and nitrogen oxides react with water in the atmosphere to form sulfuric acid and nitric acid, respectively. Both of these acids are strong acids.

Lab 18 Testing the Acidity of Aspirin

Use with Section 19.4

Objectives

▶ Measure the pH of solutions of unbuffered and buffered aspirin.
▶ Titrate each solution with a base.
▶ Make and use a graph of pH versus volume of base for the two pain relievers.

Process Skills

Collecting and interpreting data, comparing and contrasting, hypothesizing, making and using graphs, measuring and using numbers

Time Allotment

1 class period

Data and Observations (Lab 17)   Sample Data

Data Table 1							
Well	Acid	Initial [Acid] (*M*)	pH	[H$^+$] at equilibrium (*M*)	[Acid] at equilibrium (*M*)	K_a	Average K_a
A1	boric acid	1.00×10^{-1}	5.1	7.9×10^{-6}	1.0×10^{-1}	6.2×10^{-10}	8.1×10^{-10}
A3	boric acid	1.00×10^{-3}	6.0	1.0×10^{-6}	1.0×10^{-3}	1.0×10^{-9}	
B1	citric acid	1.00×10^{-1}	2.1	7.9×10^{-3}	9.2×10^{-2}	6.8×10^{-4}	5.9×10^{-4}
B3	citric acid	1.00×10^{-3}	3.3	5.0×10^{-4}	5.0×10^{-4}	5.0×10^{-4}	
C1	hydrogen peroxide	1.00×10^{-1}	6.3	5.0×10^{-7}	1.0×10^{-1}	2.5×10^{-12}	3.3×10^{-12}
C3	hydrogen peroxide	1.00×10^{-3}	7.2	6.3×10^{-8}	1.0×10^{-3}	4.0×10^{-12}	
D1	permanganic acid	1.00×10^{-1}	1.0	1.0×10^{-1}	0	—	—
D3	permanganic acid	1.00×10^{-3}	3.0	1.0×10^{-3}	0	—	

Materials

See pages 11T–14T for materials.
*(Visit the Chemistry Web site at **science.glencoe.com** to find links about safety in the laboratory.)*

Alternative Materials

▶ The volume of added NaOH could be measured with a burette instead of a thin-stem pipette.
▶ A pH meter could be used instead of pH paper.

Preparation

▶ Dissolve 4.0 g NaOH in 1.00 L of distilled water to make 0.1M NaOH. Observe the required precautions for preparing and handling NaOH solutions.
▶ Unbuffered and buffered aspirin may be purchased over the counter at most stores.

Pre-Lab

1. An acid and a base react in aqueous solution to produce a salt and water.
2. A buffer is a solution that resists changes in pH when limited amounts of acid or base are added.
3. The buffer should contain 0.1 mol of the conjugate base (A^-) in the form of a salt such as NaA.
4. The equivalence point is marked by an abrupt increase in pH followed by a gradual increase in pH as more NaOH is added.
5. See Hypothesis.

Teaching the Lab

Have students work in groups of two.

▶ Demonstrate the proper use of the mortar and pestle. Instruct students to break up each tablet by gently pounding it before beginning to grind it. Have them remove the powder with a nonmetal tool, such as a plastic spoon, to avoid scratching the mortar's ceramic finish.
▶ Emphasize that students should try to make all drops the same size when they dispense water or NaOH from the thin-stem pipette.

Hypothesis

The buffered aspirin will show a smaller change in pH when base is added. The additional amount of conjugate base in the buffered aspirin resists changes in pH.

Data and Observations

See data table for sample data.

Analyze and Conclude

1. Students' graphs should be similar to the following:

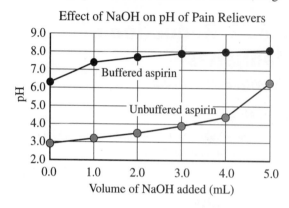

Effect of NaOH on pH of Pain Relievers

2. No, neither pain reliever was titrated to its equivalence point. Neither curve shows an abrupt increase in pH followed by a gradual increase in pH.
3. Unbuffered aspirin was more acidic.
4. Answers may vary. Results should agree with the hypothesis. Disagreements may result from inaccuracy in measuring volume by counting drops, the limited precision of pH paper, or mistakes in determining pH on the basis of the color of the paper.

Real-World Chemistry

1. Calcium carbonate dissociates into calcium ions and carbonate ions when water is present. The carbonate ions act as a base and accept hydrogen ions from tannic acid, thus neutralizing the tannic acid and protecting the DNA.

Data and Observations (Lab 18)

Sample Data

Data Table 1							
Number of drops in 1.0 mL: 14							
Pain reliever	**pH before NaOH**	**pH after adding NaOH**					**Change in pH**
		1.0 mL	**2.0 mL**	**3.0 mL**	**4.0 mL**	**5.0 mL**	
Unbuffered aspirin	2.9	3.2	3.5	3.9	4.4	6.3	3.4
Buffered aspirin	6.3	7.4	7.7	7.9	8.0	8.1	1.8

2. The amount of NaOH = (0.200 mol/L) × $(42.0 \times 10^{-3} \text{ L})$ = 8.40×10^{-3} mol. One mol of NaOH neutralizes one mol of HCOOH, so 8.40×10^{-3} mol of HCOOH is neutralized in the titration. The molarity of HCOOH = $(8.40 \times 10^{-3} \text{ mol})/(75.0 \times 10^{-3} \text{ L})$ = 0.112M.

3. The buffer tends to keep the solution near a pH that either makes the other substances in the solution work more effectively or is less irritating to the eyes.

Lab 19 Reduction of Manganese

Use with Section 20.2

Objectives
▶ Calculate a value for the molarity of the $KMnO_4$ solution using stoichiometry and volume data.
▶ Write and balance oxidation–reduction equations.

Process Skills
Observing and inferring, measuring and using numbers, predicting

Time Allotment
1 class period

Materials
See pages 11T–14T for materials.
(Visit the Chemistry Web site at **science.glencoe.com** *to find links about safety in the laboratory.)*

Alternative Materials
▶ Ferrous ammonium sulfate (corrosive) can be substituted for the sodium oxalate.
▶ Test tubes containing the reaction mixture can be anchored to a ring stand with a clamp instead of holding it with a test-tube holder.

Preparation
▶ To make the $KMnO_4$ solution, dissolve 6.32 g $KMnO_4$ in enough distilled water to make 1.00 L of solution. This solution should be made fresh the day of the experiment.
▶ To make 1.0M solution of H_2SO_4, slowly, while stirring, add 56 mL of concentrated H_2SO_4 to enough distilled water to make 1.00 L of solution. Wear safety goggles, gloves, and an apron and take care to avoid overheating by stirring.

▶ Each group will require 10 mL of the $KMnO_4$ solution and 3 mL of the H_2SO_4 solution.

Pre-Lab
1. $5C_2O_4^{2-}(aq) + 2MnO_4^-(aq) + 16H^+(aq) \rightarrow$
$10CO_2(g) + 8H_2O(l) + 2Mn^{2+}(aq)$

2. +7; +2

3. 10

4. 0.250 g of $Na_2C_2O_4$ = 1.87×10^{-3} mol; 7.48×10^{-4} mol $KMnO_4$; 0.0249M $KMnO_4$

5. If there are 24 drops in 1 mL, then 180 drops will be needed to titrate 0.10 g $Na_2C_2O_4$.

Teaching the Lab
Have students work in groups of two.
▶ Review with students the definition of an oxidation–reduction reaction. Discuss the parts of the reaction between $KMnO_4$ and $H_2C_2O_4$. Be sure students understand why the reaction involves $H_2C_2O_4$ instead of $Na_2C_2O_4$. Students should recognize that the reaction is only between the oxalate ions and the permanganate ions, while the cations are spectator ions.
▶ You may want to review calculations. Remind students to use the balanced chemical equation during stoichiometric calculations.
▶ Caution students that $KMnO_4$ stains do not wash out of clothing and must wear off the skin. They must wear proper protection.
▶ Use non-mercury based thermometers.

Hypothesis
C is oxidized and Mn is reduced.

Data and Observations
See data tables.
1. (23 + 24 + 25)/3 = 24 drops/mL
2. 192 drops/24 drops per mL = 8.0 mL = 8.0×10^{-3} L
3. 2(22.99 g/mol) + 2(12.01 g/mol) + 4(16.00 g/mol) = 134.00 g/mol
4. 0.10 g $Na_2C_2O_4$/(134.00 g/ mol) = 7.5×10^{-4} mol $Na_2C_2O_4$
5. 7.5×10^{-4} mol oxalate × (2 mol permanganate/ 5 mol oxalate) = 3.0×10^{-4} mol permanganate
6. (3.0×10^{-4} mol permanganate)/(8.0×10^{-3} L permanganate solution) = 0.038M

Analyze and Conclude
1. to quantify the volume
2. Colorless; pink/purple; at the endpoint, no oxalate ions remain to reduce the permanganate ions.

Data and Observations (Lab 19)

Data Table 1				
Micropipette used for:	**Number of drops in 1 mL**			
	Trial 1	**Trial 2**	**Trial 3**	**Average**
$KMnO_4$	23	24	25	24
H_2SO_4	23	23	26	24

Data Table 2	
Mass of sodium oxalate (g)	0.10
Drops of $KMnO_4$ needed to reach endpoint	192
Volume of $KMnO_4$ needed to reach endpoint (mL)	8

3. Answers will vary, but might include errors in measuring, calculations, and visual match to the color standard (titration).

Real-World Chemistry

1. Oxidizing agent; the product, O, is in a 0 (zero) oxidation state. Oxygen tends to gain electrons to form a more stable O^{2-} ion. Thus, it would be the oxidizing agent during the bleaching action.

2. oxidizing agent; reduction

Lab 20 Plants Produce Oxygen

Use with Section 26.4

Objectives

▶ Observe the production of oxygen gas using an indicator.

▶ Relate the rate of oxygen production to carbon dioxide concentration.

▶ Infer the effect of carbon dioxide concentration on photosynthesis.

Process Skills

Observing and inferring, collecting and interpreting data, measuring and using numbers, drawing a conclusion, designing an experiment/identifying variables, thinking critically

Time Allotment

1 class period

Materials

See pages 11T–14T for materials.

*(Visit the Chemistry Web site at **science.glencoe.com** to find links about safety in the laboratory.)*

Alternative Materials

▶ Students may use *fresh* spinach leaves, leaves of tomatoes, green peas, or radishes. Avoid leaves from plants with slow photosynthetic rates, such as succulents and plants with hairy or waxy leaves.

▶ Large (deep) wells in a microplate can be substituted for test tubes and rack.

▶ If sunlight is unavailable, fluorescent lamps may be used.

▶ Performing the experiment under several different light sources and comparing the results may test the effect of light sources on photosynthesis.

Preparation

▶ To make 0.2% $NaHCO_3$ solution, dissolve 1.0 g $NaHCO_3$ in 500 mL of pH 6.8 buffer.

▶ Buffers can be purchased from science supply houses but only in whole numbers, such as pH 7. To make pH 6.8 buffer, add from an eyedropper 2 drops of $0.1M$ HCl to 500 mL of pH 7 buffer. Check the pH of the solution with a pH meter. Continue adding the HCl until a pH of 6.8 is reached. If the pH drops lower than 6.8, it can be raised using drops of $0.1M$ NaOH.

▶ Each group of students needs 2 mL of sodium hydrogen carbonate solution and 1 mL of methylene blue indicator solution.

Pre-Lab

1. See Hypothesis.

2. Chloroplasts are plant and algal organelles that contain chlorophyll. They are the site of photosynthesis in the cells of plants and algae.

3. It is a control.

4. Oxygen is the only gas that decolorizes methylene blue.

Teaching the Lab

Have students work in groups of two.

▶ Review with students the overall equation for photosynthesis.

▶ Caution students that methylene blue stains skin and clothes.

▶ Explain the purpose of an experimental control.

▶ Review why the rate of a reaction can be followed by the rate of product formation.

▶ Remind students to never place the pipette in their mouth.

Hypothesis

Because CO_2 is a reactant, photosynthesis will take place faster in $NaHCO_3$ solution than in distilled water.

Data and Observations

Student answers will vary, but should include fading of color and bubble formation. The time needed for decolorization should be around 5 to 6 min, but will depend in large part on the intensity of sunlight available. Cloudy days will take longer than sunny days.

Analyze and Conclude

1. The test tube containing $NaHCO_3$ solution; student answers will vary but should include the faster rate of decolorization.

2. The increased concentration of CO_2 increases the rate of photosynthesis.

3. 2.00×10^{-4} moles O_2; 3.41×10^{-5} moles glucose

4. Student answers will vary. One possible solution is to remove the plunger from a syringe. Place the leaf pieces in the syringe, reinsert the plunger, and fill the syringe with solution. Plug the tip of the syringe with a fingertip. The buildup of gas will push the plunger outward. You can also use a fermentation tube or any kind of setup that would collect the oxygen gas.

5. Answers will vary, but might include different quantities of leaf material in each test tube, inaccurate observations, and incorrect data recording.

Real-World Chemistry

1. The leaves of the plants can help convert the CO_2 from the exhaust gases to O_2.

2. Decolorizing the methylene blue would confirm the presence of O_2. Only O_2 decolorizes the methylene blue, so no mistake would be made about the identity of the substance.

CREDITS

Art Credits

Navta Associates: **v, 6, 18, T95, T97, T107**; Glencoe: **62**; MacArt Design: **1, 2, 14, 18, 22, 34, 38, 42, 46, 50**